The Techniques of
PEWTERSMITHING

The Techniques of
PEWTERSMITHING

Charles Hull & Jack Murrell

B T Batsford Ltd, London

ISBN 0 7134 4751 6

Typeset by Santype International Ltd., Salisbury, Wilts.
and printed in Great Britain by Butler and Tanner Ltd., Frome, Somerset.

for the publishers
B. T. Batsford Ltd.
4 Fitzhardinge Street
London W1H 0AH

Frontispiece. *Two handled covered cup in Queen Anne style 13.3 cm (5¼ in) high by Hull Pewter (Photo Francis Thompson Studios Ltd). The covered cup is interesting in that it is probably the first pewter to be cast under vacuum, using silicone rubber moulds. In this case, the mould was mounted in a vacuum tank and the pewter fed in from the outside. The advantage with this technique is that there is no problem in requiring the pewter to eject the air from the mould, so the filling of the cavity is extremely rapid. The speed of filling the mould enables very thin wall sections to be cast for the piece, whilst at the same time keeping the metal temperature low – in this case 250°C (482°F). Detail finish is very fine and little finishing other than buffing is required.*

Contents

Acknowledgements   7
Foreword   9
Introduction   11

I   A brief history of pewter
Introduction   13
The Worshipful Company of Pewterers   14
Status of pewter   16
Decline of pewtercraft   17
Sheffield pewter   18
Art Nouveau   19
Resurgence   19
Europe   19
USA   22
Malaysia   24
Japan   24
Summary   24

II   The metal
Introduction   25
Alloying   25
Rolling   26
Remelting   26
Different alloys   26
Conclusion   28

III   Design and application
Designing pewterware   29
Working drawings   32

IV   Workshop tools and equipment
Workshop   37
Tools and equipment   38
Hand tools   42

V   Soldering
Introduction   47
Solder   47
Fluxes   47
Technique   48
Summary   52

VI   Hand-forming techniques
Introduction   53
Round bowl and porringer   53
Cylindrical tobacco jar   56
Bud vase   57
Hip flasks   59
Circular flasks   60
Boxes   61
Small boxes   63
Deep bowls   64
Conical jar with lid   66
Trays   66
Other hand processes   68
Simple spouts   68
Developed spout   69
Handles   69
Profiling   69
Repairing pewter   70
Antique pewter repair (Stanley Shemmel)   71
The individual approach   72
Summary   73

VII   Spinning and spunware
Spinning   74
Spunware   82
Conclusion   88

VIII   Casting
Introduction   90
Melting pot   90
Metal mould casting   91
Slush casting   98
Silicone rubber mould casting   100
Centrifugal rubber mould casting   106
Lost wax casting   113
Vulcanised rubber mould casting   118
Cuttlefish bone casting   118
Sand casting   120
Plaster castings   125
Pressure die casting   129
Permanent metal moulds   130
Faults and problems   130
General health and safety   133

IX **Finishing**
 Introduction   134
 Equipment   134
 Technique   135
 Summary   138
 Care and maintenance   138
 Cleaning antique pewter (Stanley Shemmel) 139
 Electrolytic cleaning (Ronald F. Homer)   140

X   **Decorative techniques**
 Introduction   141
 Decoration by raising the surface   141
 Decoration by removal of metal   145
 Roller printing   153
 Plain surface treatment   153

Glossary
Tables and conversions
 Conversion factors   157
 Pewter alloys   158
 Pewter sheet   158
 Melting points   159
 Polishing speeds   159
Sources of supply
 United Kingdom suppliers   160
 Italy suppliers   162
 United States of America suppliers   162
Bibliography
 Technical   163
 Historical   163
Index   165

Acknowledgements

This book could not have been undertaken without the generous help and advice given by a large number of manufacturers and individual craftsmen in Britain, Europe, the USA and Malaysia, and our profound thanks are due to all those who gave up so much of their time on our behalf.

It is a marvellous experience to discuss the techniques of the crafts with people who have in many cases spent their whole working lives in the trade and to watch them at work forming, turning, soldering and engraving with consumate skill and speed.

We have visited the following manufacturers.

In England:

Englefields	London
Abbey Pewter	London
Buckingham Pewter	London
James Smellie	Birmingham
George Johnson & Co.	Birmingham
A. E. Williams	Birmingham
Haseler and Restall	Birmingham
Tether Manufacturing	Sheffield
PMC	Sheffield
James Dixon	Sheffield
I. Gibson & Sons	Sheffield
Frys Metals	London
Connell & Yardley – Engravers	London
Tom Neal	Barnard Castle
Minutia Models Ltd	Worcester
Phoenix Model Developments	Northampton

On the Continent:

Potstainiers Hutois	Belgium
Daalderop	Holland
Grenningloh	Germany

In the USA:

Gibson Pewter	Hartford, USA

In Malaysia:

Selangor Pewter	Kuala Lumpur

Much information has also been gathered by correspondence and discussion and our grateful thanks are due to:
David Innis and Derek Weeks of Englefields
John Webster and Ron Channer of Abbey Pewter
Ken Targett of Buckingham Pewter
Robert Ruppel and Howard Hopkins of James Smellie
A. and D. Williams of A. E. Williams
Ken Hamblin of Haseler and Restall
Alan Aikin of PMC
Peter Tether of Tether Manufacturing
James Porteous and Jim Dorling of James Dixon
N. Edwards of Granville College
Larry O'Connell of O'Connell and Yardley
Pik Yong of Selangor Pewter
Charles C. Stieff of Stieff Pewter
Lee R. Titcomb of Woodbury Pewter
P. Duchene of Les Etains des Postanniers Hutois
Jan W. Van Meurs of the Netherlands Tin Guild
Elise M. Ramsay of Lincoln
C. Haak of Daalderop
Brian H. Chislett of Clevedon Pewter
G. Gross of Etains de Paris
S. Schmerbeck of Grenningloh
D. Robbins and D. Muller of the Tin Research Institute
Raymond Gibson of Gibson Pewter

To Bill Kayhoe who is the complete pewter craftsman, we offer our sincere thanks for his help on a whole range of techniques and the supply of reference books and photographs. To Wayne Hilt for his observations on the repair of antique pewter, and particularly to Stanley Shemmel and Ron Homer of the Pewter Society for allowing us to reprint part of their article on the repair and cleaning of antique pewter.

Our gratitude to Shirley Charron for allowing us to use photographs of her work and that of Frances Felton; to Dr and Mrs Melvyn D. Wolf for photographs from their fine collection of William Will

7

pewter; to Ron Chivrall for his help in model-making; to the Worshipful Company of Pewterers who have generously allowed us to use photographs of pieces from their collection and helped to provide many valuable contacts in the trade and elsewhere.

Except where stated in the captions, all of the photographs were taken by Jack Murrell. Particular thanks go to David Payne who processed and printed over 1,000 photographs during the preparation of this book, and also to Jack Smith for his photographs; to Mike Martin for his German translations; to Allen Blower and Dudley Robins for their advice on the characteristics of various alloys and to John Hull for his comments on metallurgy generally and his work on a range of experiments conducted on vacuum casting. Equipment suppliers were very helpful in the provision of information and catalogues and on some occasions, tools and materials. These companies are acknowledged also in the list of suppliers.

Our thanks to our respective wives who typed, revised and retyped the copy, corrected the English and spelling and made allowances, almost without complaint, for the vast amount of paperwork which spreads throughout the house when three-year projects of this nature are undertaken.

Our acknowledgements also go to Batsford for their patience and advice in preparing this book.

Charles Hull
Jack Murrell

Jack Murrell has taken the main burden of this book, writing up all the technical data, making the sketches and photographing the various techniques described and my sincere thanks go to him for this prodigious effort.

Finally, I would like to thank Robert Parker my travelling companion without whose persistent nagging this book would never have been written – he may have a lot to answer for.

Charles Hull

Foreword

by the Chairman of the Association
of Pewter Craftsmen

The Association of British Pewter Craftsmen was formed in 1970 by the manufacturers and metal suppliers to ensure the maintenance of standards of quality and material by their members. With a view to providing the continuity of these high standards, the Association, with the active support of the Worshipful Company of Pewterers, is encouraging the reintroduction of apprenticeships within the trade as well as the provision of skills' testing for pewterers in training. Pewter manufactured by members is marked with the quality mark of the Association – make sure you look for it when buying a piece of pewter.

It is the Association's aim to increase public awareness of the great versatility and attractiveness of pewter. This book provides an insight into the possibilities of working in pewter; I hope it will encourage the craft colleges to add pewter to their metalwork courses and also attract craftsmen in other materials to test their skills in pewter – the potential of the material is almost limitless.

Allen Blower

Introduction

Few people today have any conception of the part played by pewtercraft in the social and economic life of Britain between the fifteenth and eighteenth centuries. By the middle of the seventeenth century pewter was second only to cloth in the value of its exports. By the end of the seventeenth century, the pewter in circulation (estimated at over 30,000 tons) would be valued on today's retail prices at £1,000 million, with over £100 million worth being produced annually. When one considers that the population then was probably only one-tenth of its present level, these figures become truly staggering.

Today, sadly, pewter does not receive its due and justified attention. Everyone has heard of the pewter tankard, but how many people are aware of the full range of domestic items, from spoons to chargers 33 in. in diameter, from candlesticks to gallon measures, from goblets to coffee- and teapots, from chalices to salts, that have been made in pewter. The list is almost endless, and yet today little antique pewter remains and the tankard must be the principal product.

Pewter is the most adaptable of materials. It can be melted on a gas ring (liquidus 240°C, 464°F) and cast into steel, cast iron, bronze, plaster, sand, cuttlefish, nitrile or silicone rubber moulds. It can be turned on a simple woodworking lathe. In sheet form, it can be spun-formed on a lathe, press-formed in wooden and metal dies and as silver or copper, it can be hand-beaten with hammers of metal, wood, leather or plastic with the added advantage that it does not suffer from work-hardening, so avoiding the annealing stage required for other metals. It is readily solderable or weldable with iron or torch for those with average skill. It requires cleaning only once or twice a year.

As with silver, it is a genuine craft metal and has never really been adapted to the techniques of mass production, many manufacturers using basically the same techniques practised in the trade for centuries. Admittedly, it is a rather expensive material containing at least 90% tin and can be roughly costed at five to six times that of copper but about one-thirtieth the price of silver. In its favour, however, it can be claimed that there is no waste – faulty castings can be remelted and off-cuts from the sheet can also be transferred to the melting pot.

Its finish can be regulated to personal taste from a high gloss silver shine to a warm lustre or matt surface. It can be antiqued or coloured without difficulty and is ideally suited to chasing and engraving.

So why is it not more widely used in the craft colleges and by the individual craftsman – is it that perhaps the material is just not understood or appreciated? We hope that this book may help to remedy this state of affairs and may encourage you to have a go yourself.

We have described as fully as possible all techniques currently employed by the manufacturers and a number of others that are more suited to the production of one-offs or prototypes. As with any craft, the description of the hand-forming and finishing procedures is extremely difficult, as results depend so much on delicacy of application and feel, so that patience and above all practice is the only way to achieve the desired effect. To the beginner, we would say: do not be discouraged when you see the experienced craftsman taking perhaps only a fraction of the time you spend in achieving the desired results. Everything will come with practice. Skilled craftsmen always develop particular techniques of their own to achieve specific results and we hope that those who read this book may be generous enough to share these with us so that any reprints may be continually revised as new procedures come to light.

Fig. I:1 *One of the five touchplates recording the marks of the Master Pewterers from 1666 in the possession of the Worshipful Company of Pewterers.*

We have touched briefly on low pressure and vacuum casting into silicone rubber moulds, as we feel that these techniques will be further developed in the future, and may well eventually form part of the commercial manufacturers' procedures.

However, great enjoyment and interest can be achieved with a minimum of inexpensive equipment and the opportunities for the individual practising in garage or kitchen – if one has an understanding partner – seem to be boundless. It is hoped that this emphasis on simple equipment will encourage schools, colleges and individual craftsmen to look afresh at pewter as a craft material. Pewterers are proud of their products and their craftwork and the examples shown and described in this book clearly justify their pride.

We have included a short chapter on the history of pewter to try to place the craft in its proper position in the order of things when, for a brief period, it was Britain's second most valuable manufactured export. However, for those solely interested in the history of the craft, this is not the book to buy – the appendix lists the books to be read to gain this knowledge.

Perhaps surprisingly pewter in Britain and Europe is still predominantly regarded as a traditional material and nearly all designs marketed today are reproductions or similar in style to designs of 100–300 years ago. The writers feel that this is a pity as the material, in a similar way to silver, proved eminently successful in converting to the Art Nouveau designs introduced at the turn of this century and would, in our view, be equally successful for developing new ideas in shape and form today. Again, we hope that some modern designers may be encouraged to experiment with pewter to express their thoughts.

Because for the individual it is often difficult to know where to buy the materials and equipment necessary to take the first step, we include in the appendices a list of outlets and manufacturers to meet initial needs. A list of recommended equipment is also included together with useful conversion tables.

In the text we describe craftsmen as both pewterers and pewtersmiths. Certainly pewterers is the much older term, but it does seem that by the end of the eighteenth century pewtersmith also came to be used, perhaps particularly where the craftsman was working in close proximity to other workers in metal – silversmiths and coppersmiths. In Sheffield pewter craftsmen were sometimes described as white-metalsmiths (whitesmiths) and indeed white-metal today that contains a minimum of 90% tin would also qualify as pewter.

Whether you call yourself a pewterer or a pewtersmith is not important. Get hold of an ingot and some pewter sheet and try a simple casting or working the sheet by hand. In a very short time we believe you will find yourself 'hooked' on the formation and versatility of the material which has been worked by craftsmen for well over 2000 years.

I A Brief History of Pewter

INTRODUCTION

The purpose of this book is to describe the techniques and practices of the pewter craftsman, but to understand the versatility of the material and its wide potential it is helpful to have at least some background knowledge of the long and fascinating history of the craft and its changes in fortune and direction.

It is not certain when the first pewter articles were made, but it would seem that tin alloys were known and worked from the time of the earliest recorded history.

The oldest piece of pewter so far positively dated is a two-handled flask of *c*.1400 BC from an Egyptian grave at Abydos. The analysis of the metal used is extremely interesting – 93% tin, 6% lead, 1% copper – which would have been accepted in Britain as a suitable grade for holloware as late as the eighteenth or even the nineteenth centuries.

Although it is sometimes suggested that the tin mines in Cornwall encouraged the Romans to invade Britain, to augment their supply of tin for the manufacture of bronze, they do not appear to have developed this potential until the latter half of their occupation. There is no evidence that pewterware was manufactured in England prior to the occupation, and in fact no Romano-British pewter found can be dated with certainty prior to *c*.250 AD.

It is probable from the number of pieces found that there was a pewter industry of reasonable size existing for the last 200 years or so of the Roman occupation. Sadly, there is no written evidence to draw on and the pieces themselves give no clue to the chronological development of the craft, although it is clear that considerable skill and sophistication in design was achieved. The number of manufacturing centres is not known, but the wide spread of the finds in the West Country, London and East Anglia and the variety of the alloys used, suggests it is likely that there were several.

As well as hand-forming, the Romans cast and machined their pewter. Limestone moulds have been found on a site at Camerton near Bath (with their skill in bronze work it is not inconceivable that they could have developed the use of metal moulds for their holloware items, although there is no evidence for this) and a number of plates and other pieces show tool marks from turning on a form of lathe. In fact, the finish on some Roman pewter and the variety of design including engraving work is remarkable in that it would suggest that they must have developed, albeit in perhaps a rather primitive form, a number of the techniques used consistently by the craftsmen in pewter over the centuries. As presumably the Egyptians before them, the Romans discovered that the addition of lead improved the durability and hardness of tin, although the alloys used vary widely from 15% to over 50% of lead. From this evidence it would appear that no specific standards of the alloy were laid down, as was to happen with such precision in later years.

With the departure of the Romans nothing is heard of the craft in England for almost 600 years, though with the scarcity of information generally for this period it cannot be said with certainty that the craft completely disappeared, and certain ornaments that can be dated to this period appear to be made of some form of tin alloy.

Ecclesiastical records of the early Norman period refer to the making of chalices and patens of tin, a word which would have described pewter in these times, and a pair of extremely finely made pewter cruets from Ludlow and Weoley are attributed to the fourteenth century, as is a small dish and lidded jug excavated at Tong Castle. These early datings tend to be a little circumspect due to the paucity of available pieces.

It would seem that the revival of the pewter industry on a reasonable scale followed the general development of the craft guilds from the beginning of the fourteenth century and records begin to describe craftsmen specifically as pewterers rather than as metalworkers who may also have worked in pewter. The growth of the industry from this date however was rapid, particularly in London, followed closely by York and a number of other provincial centres. It is interesting to note that before the middle of the fourteenth century tin production in Cornwall was averaging over 500 tons per annum, and the pewter industry must have been absorbing an increasing proportion of this output.

It is evident that the pewter industry in Europe developed in a similarly spectacular fashion, even perhaps at a slightly earlier date, indicating a significant, widespread change in the economic and social conditions of the period.

That the pewterers in London joined together for their common protection and control of the craft can be seen as early as 1348 with the granting of ordinances. These ordinances were remarkably comprehensive in scope covering the technical requirements and standards of manufacture and also rules for membership of the 'fraternity'.

The steady growth of the industry and its control within the guilds continued throughout the fourteenth and early fifteenth centuries with the main provincial centres being York, Bristol, Norwich and Coventry. By the mid-fifteenth century most regional centres must have included at least one practising pewterer.

THE WORSHIPFUL COMPANY OF PEWTERERS

The middle of the fifteenth century saw a high level of British pewter exports to Europe, mainly sustained by London pewterers whose reputation for consistent quality, assured by the many ordinances and statutes introduced over the previous 50 years, gave Britain, for a short period, a pre-eminent position in the pewtercraft in Europe.

That pewter held a significant position in the rapidly expanding economy of the country is underlined by the granting of the first Royal Charter by Edward IV in 1474, which provided the London Guild with legal control of the industry throughout England, with powers which by today's standards could be regarded as extreme and arbitrary. There is no doubt that the guilds were set up primarily for the protection of the craft members, although the controls introduced also provided a measure of protection for the public at large.

In pewtercraft the standards of the alloy used and quality of manufacture could vary considerably without it being immediately evident to the purcha-

ser. The London Guild, which subsequent to its charter became known as the Worshipful Company of Pewterers, laid down standards, which in turn were approved and followed by the other main manufacturing centres and although modified from time to time, were to remain in force and to a great extent followed by the craft for something over 200 years. Although not all instituted in the charter of 1474, some being a continuation of earlier local ordinances and some being introduced later as necessity arose, the Company sought to control the activities and standards of the craft in very great detail indeed. To illustrate this one only has to look at a few of the major controls introduced and followed through. Perhaps the most interesting one from the present-day craftsman's point of view is the laying down of alloy standards for the manufacture of various types of products. It would seem even by the end of the fifteenth century the craft had split into three main types of manufacturer, with individual pewterers generally producing in only a single area.

The first group of pewterers, who seem to have been most highly regarded, were the manufacturers of flatware or sadware which consisted of chargers, plates, bowls, porringers, etc., which were required to be made in 'fine' metal, described as tin with as much copper as it will absorb, which would probably not be more than 2%.

It is thought that fine metal also had a small percentage of bismuth added to increase hardness, although this is not confirmed in the Company records. The second group were workers in holloware, which referred to flagons, tankards, cruets, candlesticks, some types of basins and measures, funnels, candle moulds, etc., which were produced in 'trifling' metal (trifle) which appears to have contained about 4% lead. There was also a third grade of metal, known as 'ley', which allowed for a higher lead content – about 16% for some wine measures and certain types of chamber pots, syringes, children's toys, buttons, etc. The constituents of these metals and the designation of the items to be made in the particular grades seems to have varied somewhat over the years with the standard of metal used, the standard gradually being raised – i.e. requiring less lead – until the end of the eighteenth century. A standard was also laid down for the solder used for assembling bodies and the adding of handles and feet. In addition, the Company laid down standard weights for various items in constant manufacture such as bowls, dishes, plates, basins, tea and coffee pots, porringers, tankards, spoons, chamberpots, wine measures, etc.

Certain standards of manufacturing techniques were introduced, for instance, pressing or spinning was prohibited and the booges of plates were required to be hammered. The reason for this is not absolutely clear, but the precision with which the hammering was done by some craftsmen is remarkable to see. The flatware makers, or hammermen as they were sometimes known, were regarded as the élite of the craft, possibly because the casting of large chargers – the largest known are 33 inches in diameter – must have been the most difficult technique of the craft and the flatware makers were required to use the highest grade of metal.

With so much of the pewterer's work resulting from the replacement of damaged or worn pieces – part-exchange pewter was only about one-third the price of new – from the beginning of the sixteenth century the Company required all pewter to be marked with the maker's touch, so that the pewterer taking in scrap in exchange could be assured of the quality. Of immense historical interest are the five touchplates still preserved at Pewterers Hall in London, recording the marks of some 1,100 master pewterers struck since the Great Fire of London in 1666.

These touchmarks were also required for the Company in manufacture to ensure its standards were being maintained and to identify the makers of substandard ware. They were essential in the countrywide searches it undertook to inspect pewter for sale where their authority was considerable in that the Company was empowered to confiscate 'false' pewter – i.e. that which did not meet the standard in metal or weight of piece – and fine the offender on the spot. Accurate weighing equipment must have been required for checking the metal specification as a small pellet was cast of the manufacturer's metal and weighed against a similar pellet to the Company's standard and if heavier, it could be shown that the lead content was too high.

Needless to say, the Company's inspectors were not always too popular and news of their approach often preceded them. Records of the searches show literally hundreds of pewterers were checked in this way and much substandard pewter found. The London pewterers tended to fare worst in this respect, being checked up to five times a year.

Confiscated pewter was afterwards sold to the Freemen of the Company to be brought back to standard, thereby more than covering the cost of these searches.

The London Guild, however, did much to protect its craftsmen by lobbying Parliament to prevent imports of finished goods and endeavouring to reduce the export of raw tin. It did its best to maintain the leadership of London in the industry by limiting the number of apprentices to an amount which could be absorbed within the City and discouraged pewterers from moving to the provinces. This move would probably have also been beneficial to the country pewterers as it helped to balance the number of practising pewterers with the current

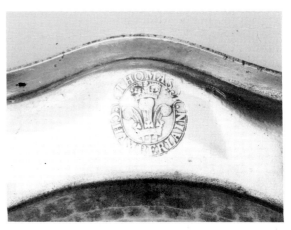

Fig. I:2 *Hammering on the back of the booge on a wavy edge plate c.1740. (Courtesy of the Worshipful Company of Pewterers)*

Fig. I:3 *Assaying tool for taking samples of pewter for weighing against the company standard. (Courtesy of the Worshipful Company of Pewterers)*

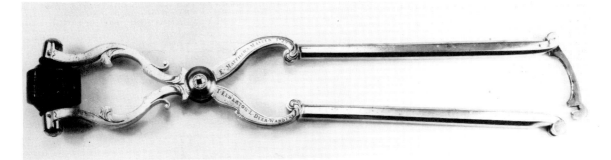

demand for their products. They forbade pewterers to use unskilled labour or those who were not 'free' of the Company and it tried, generally, to prohibit foreign craftsmen from setting up in business.

In this, the Company was not fully successful and, in fact, the influence of a few Huguenot craftsmen who came to England did result in the inclusion of antimony in the mix of 'fine' metal adopted by a number of pewterers for their extra high-quality flatware towards the end of the seventeenth century, and sometimes described on the piece with a label 'Superfine Hard Metal'.

At this distance of time it is difficult to be sure how effective on a countrywide basis the controls of the Company really were, but it is safe to conclude that they did much to achieve the high regard in which English pewter was held throughout Europe at the time and later in America.

Whilst there were local provincial guilds, these took a lead from the Company in London. One of the interesting results of this overall control from London appears to have been the relative standardisation of design throughout the country with often only marginal local detail variations giving clues to the provenance of a piece if no recorded mark is found.

The craft in Scotland, controlled by the Guild of Hammermen, produced a very different and distinctive range of designs. On the Continent, where the authority rested with the provincial guilds, local variations in form are also often quite marked.

STATUS OF PEWTER

For all its charm of colour, feel and elegance, pewter in England was, with very few exceptions, never really regarded as anything but domestic ware throughout the sixteenth, seventeenth and eighteenth centuries. The plain, solid and clean lines of the resulting pieces must be one of the reasons for the enormous interest – and high prices – antique pewter now enjoys.

The exception to this was the introduction, in the latter half of the seventeenth century, of wriggle-work engraving, achieved by rocking a sharp chisel-faced tool on the surface to produce a zigzag pattern, chiefly for commemoration pieces, such as the restoration of the monarchy in 1660 and some cast decoration on beakers and porringers. In comparison with total production, these pieces, however,

Fig. I:4 *Reproduction Mary Rose flagon, Englefields Ltd, London. (Photo: Francis Thompson Studios Ltd)*

Fig. I:5 *Porringer with cast decoration c.1700. (Courtesy of the Worshipful Company of Pewterers)*

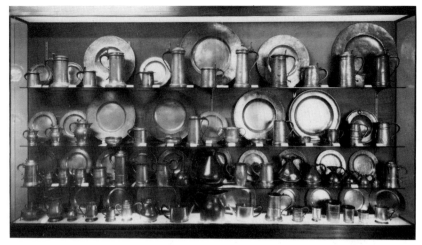

Fig. I:6 *Showcase of antique pewter at Pewterers' Hall. (Courtesy of the Worshipful Company of Pewterers)*

Fig. I:7 *Stuart candlesticks c.1675. (Courtesy of the Worshipful Company of Pewterers)*

are relatively rare and can never have formed a significant part of the overall production of pewter in England. Sadly, the utilitarian practical nature of the products and the relatively high value of the material has meant that very little antique pewter has survived especially considering that in the seventeenth century possibly 3,000 to 4,000 tons was being produced annually.

In London alone there were some 300 to 400 master pewterers mostly operating from their own 'shop' with possibly only a single journeyman or apprentice for assistance – a true craft industry in every sense of the term. It is known that sometimes a widow would continue with her husband's business.

The range of articles made was prodigious and it is not possible to show here anything but the briefest idea of what was being produced in the seventeenth and eighteenth centuries. On the Continent, however, pewter was often used for ceremonial or special pieces with much more emphasis being given to cast and engraved decoration, and a number of remarkable examples of this superlative craftsmanship have survived.

DECLINE OF PEWTERCRAFT

The influence and control of the Worshipful Company of Pewterers waned rapidly, particularly outside London, from the first quarter of the eighteenth century. The decline of the Company's control of the craft coincided with decreasing trade which was quite rapid, starting immediately after what is thought to have been its most prosperous period, from the middle to the end of the seventeenth century when the introduction of new designs was prolific. The reasons for this dramatic decline are complex, but there is no doubt that the introduction of new techniques in the manufacture of pottery and glassware played a significant part.

The ever-reducing volume of business prompted fierce competition between pewterers – previously prohibited by the Company – and inevitably, the Company's influence waned. The industrial revolution also had the effect of moving the main manufacturing centre from London to the Midlands, Wigan and later to Sheffield, where new techniques were more readily available and acceptable away from the rather reactionary influence of the Company. This change of environment saw the

Fig. I:8 *Britannia metal teapot c.1850, Broadhead and Atkin, Sheffield. (Courtesy of the Worshipful Company of Pewterers) (left)*

Fig. I:9 *'Tudric' art nouveau teaset c.1900. (right)*

Fig. I:10 *Tea and coffee service, PMC Ltd, Sheffield. (opposite left)*

Fig. I:11 *Commemoration tankards, I. Gibson & Son, Sheffield. (The tankards are spun from 0.051-inch thick sheet giving a finished weight of approximately 1¼ lb equivalent to that of a cast tankard.) (opposite right)*

development of a new type of pewter-manufacture, covering all types of product, flatware and holloware, under one roof with a more modern approach to production methods. The improved distribution facilities available also demonstrated the potential of economies of scale. Pre-eminent in this field must have been the Duncombe business in Bewdley, whose considerable variety of operation and output is only now being appreciated. It has been said that in a random collection of mid-eighteenth- to early nineteenth-century pewter, 50% is likely to emanate from the Duncombe factory.

SHEFFIELD PEWTER

From the beginning of the nineteenth century Sheffield, too, developed a quite remarkable pewter industry, which was to dominate production throughout the century and, indeed, is still the major pewter-manufacturing centre in England. The techniques used were in effect totally different from those of the industry up to that time, employing the methods of the silversmith and possibly more particularly that of the Sheffield plate-manufacturer – Sheffield plate is made up of a copper sheet base on to which has been rolled a thin sheet of silver fused

on to the copper to produce a workable sheet of bimetal. Items of great variety and complexity were made from cold rolled pewter sheet – itself rolled from cast ingots – and formed in the press on wooden or metal dies. Appendages such as handles, spouts or feet were either formed or cast and soldered to the body in the normal way.

The constituents of the sheet, which is often described under the generic name of Britannia metal, after the 'Britannia Metal Works' of A. Vickers, the pioneer of the process, are very similar to that of Superfine Hard Metal, with a little extra copper to improve ductility and possibly to stop the antimony, which is not fully soluble in the alloy, migrating to the surface when the original ingot is cast. The range of products made in Sheffield was extremely wide, the designs being different from anything produced in pewter previously, closely copying those of the more expensive Sheffield plate and silverware. Until fairly recently Britannia metalware has been somewhat discounted by the pewter collector, perhaps because it is much lighter and more delicate than traditional cast pewterware of earlier times. Also, many of the designs are ornate, particularly so with the wide range of coffee- and teasets made, which accord with the fashion of the Victorian period; but while studying the methods and techniques of manufacture, it is impossible not to be impressed by the quality and skill of the craftsmanship. The scale of the pewter trade in Sheffield in the nineteenth century was considerable, leading manufacturers such as Dixon and Sons and Broadhead and Atkin employing several hundred men, including both chasers and engravers.

Despite this infusion of new techniques and production methods, by the end of the nineteenth century the industry had again shrunk considerably

in size, now being almost completely centred in Sheffield, with some of the more traditional pewter still being made in Birmingham and perhaps a further one or two pewterers remaining in London.

ART NOUVEAU

The emergence at the end of the nineteenth century of Art Nouveau designs again gave the industry the opportunity to show the versatility of pewter. It is, perhaps, in Germany that we see the greatest expression of this movement, and it is German pewter craftsmen who realised most fully the considerable potential the metal has for being easily cast into the flowing lines and shapes of the designs.

In England, Liberty's, who were active in promoting modern design, commissioned a number of leading designers in this field and had pieces made in both pewter and silver. Their Tudric pewter range is now relatively scarce, but during the short period just prior to the end of the nineteenth century and the first decade of the twentieth, it enjoyed great popularity. The quality of the Liberty pewter, produced by J. H. Haseler in Birmingham, was excellent and some of the designs clearly show the versatility and adaptability of the material.

RESURGENCE

Today, the pewter industry appears again to be showing the adaptability and resource of its forbears and, whilst relying heavily on the designs of the past, modern designers are becoming aware of the potential the material has to offer.

The nature of the material and the wide range of items now being produced in pewter ensures that it will always be a craft-based industry, with inevitably a great deal of individual handwork being required.

To ensure high standards of workmanship are retained leading manufacturing countries have in recent years been forming trade associations, laying down standards for the craft not so very far removed from those of the old guilds. In England in 1970 the Association of British Pewter Craftsmen was formed by leading manufacturers for this purpose, the Association being closely connected and supported by the Pewterers' Company in London. Similar associations have also been formed in Holland, Germany, Belgium, Italy and the USA to ensure that standards are maintained, particularly in regard to the constituents of the metal, which in these 'hygienic' days must be kept within fairly tight limits and certainly must not contain more than 0.5% lead.

The individual craft associations in Europe have also joined together to form the European Pewter Union to ensure a common approach to requirements of the EEC legislation, so we are now seeing closer links throughout this craft industry than has been achieved over the last 600 years.

EUROPE

It seems likely that the town guilds in Europe began to be formed at a rather earlier date than in England, but as their development did not finally result in any form of centralised control of the pewter craft, as with the Worshipful Company of Pewterers in London, regional differences in the style and type of the pewterware produced continued throughout the period of the guilds' influence and even, to some extent, into the present time where the proliferation of designs is far greater than in Britain. Again, little domestic European pewter has survived, in spite of the prodigious quantities

Fig. I:12 *A spun teapot, James Dixon & Sons, Sheffield. (left)*

Fig. I:13 *Decanter, PMC Ltd, Sheffield. (below)*

Fig. I:14 *A spun plate warmer, Tether Manufacturing Ltd, Sheffield. (right)*

that must have been produced. Styles tended to be modified gradually from one area to the next, so that national frontiers did not provide dramatic changes in form.

Although English pewter was held in very high regard in Europe in the seventeenth century for its quality, there is no doubt that the Continental pewterer was equally skilled, particularly in regard to the 'special' and ceremonial pieces made, which appear never to have been a particular requirement of the English market – no highly ornamented pieces were produced in England, even though a few Huguenot pewterers came to England at the beginning of the seventeenth century. As European pewter is such an enormous subject in itself, we will have to confine our comments to one or two of the fine ceremonial pieces that have survived in reasonable numbers for us to marvel at today.

François Briot is perhaps pre-eminent in this respect and his 'Temperance' dish of 1590 demonstrates that pewterers of the sixteenth century had achieved a skill in their craft that has probably never been surpassed.

The spread of Huguenot craftsmen from France throughout Europe at the end of the seventeenth century did much to influence the design of pewterware, particularly in regard to pieces with relief cast decoration.

Fig. I:15 *'Temperance' dish of 1590, François Briot.* *(Courtesy of Victoria and Albert Museum)*

Fig. I:16 *Seventeenth-century German guild flagons.* *(Courtesy of Victoria and Albert Museum)*

Fig. I:17 *Reproduction in pewter of a seventeenth-century German silver flagon, Grenningloh, Hemer, West Germany. (Photo: Grenningloh)*

Again, the influence of silver designs can clearly be seen in these pieces as it has been to a great extent throughout the history of the craft both in England and the Continent. Although manufactured throughout Europe, Germany was the greatest exponent of these decorated styles of pewterware, with Nuremberg possibly being the major centre for its manufacture. The skill of the engravers and mould-makers of the time must have been of an extremely high order and shows that if the skills and the experience are there, there is virtually no limit to the adaptability of the metal. The main items to have received the attentions of the Continental pewterers for these specialist designs are the huge Guild flagons and plates, but there are also impressive pieces in tankards, wine and water jugs and porringers, whose elaborate handles or ears, as well as cast decoration and gadrooning, makes one wonder if these pieces held some special family significance both in England and Europe.

The guilds in Europe appear to have influenced the pewter trade very much as in England, and much pewterware is stamped with the maker's mark, with also perhaps a quality mark, which often helps to establish the provenance and date of a piece and

Fig. I:18 *Tankards by William Will from the collection of Dr and Mrs Melvyn D. Wolf.*

Fig. I:19 *Flagon – Aaronsburg type by William Will from the collection of Dr and Mrs Melvyn D. Wolf.*

greatly adds to the attraction for the collector.

Germany was also the leading exponent of Art Nouveau designs, which became so enormously popular at the turn of the nineteenth century. A number of leading artists of the time used pewter to express their ideas, it having proved very adaptable to the flowing designs of the vogue.

Pewterware has retained its place in the public appreciation in Europe to a greater extent than in Britain and today a wide range of traditional cast decorated ware is still manufactured. The techniques used today are probably very similar to those of earlier centuries, except that the moulds are now of steel, where they were probably previously of bronze and the turning is likely to be on large copying lathes instead of the original hand-held tool lathes of the past.

France, Holland, Germany, Switzerland, Italy and Scandinavia all have their craftsmen in pewter, so that the collector of contemporary pewterware has the widest possible choice available.

USA

Pewterware from America of course begins from a much later date, the early pewterers being much hampered by controls exercised from England, forbidding the exports of raw tin both before and after Independence. For this reason the quality of metal in some early American pewter is not up to European standards, as it was probably made from scrap materials, with possibly some addition of lead to make up the shortage of metal that must have existed.

Having said this, however, there is no doubt that the pewter from the best American craftsmen was well up to the standard of their 'cousins' in Europe and many notable pieces remain to demonstrate their skill.

Understandably, the style of pieces in the main follows closely those of the English pewterers, although often being several decades behind the current fashion in England. Perhaps from an English viewpoint the most notable of these pewterers was William Will, who, although coming from German stock, adopted English styles for his pewterware. All his pewterware was of exemplary quality and he must be particularly noted for his coffee- and tea pots which are exceptional.

As in England, where the centre of the trade moved from London to the industrial Midlands during the eighteenth century, which also saw the formation of larger companies encompassing the manufacture of all types of pewterware, so in the USA emerged the Danforth family who must compare very much with the Duncombes of England in producing large quantities of cast pewter

and later as Danforth and Boardman, producing also Britannia metalware of great variety.

High-quality pewterware is still being produced by American craftsmen today and special mention must be made of an area where their craftsmanship is unsurpassed anywhere – that of hand-formed works of individual commissions in strikingly modern designs. Frances Felton's work must be the most outstanding in this field and she has now been followed by a number of her protegées who continue in this work. Would that we in Europe could also develop specialised craftsmen of this calibre. It is to be hoped that an increased awareness of the potential of pewter will encourage commissions for individual pieces in both modern and traditional styles.

Fig. I:20 *Reproduction of an eighteenth-century American teapot, William F. Kayhoe. (Photo: W. F. Kayhoe) (top left)*

Fig. I:21 *Spun pewter goblets, Raymond E. Gibson, Providence, USA. (Photo: Gibson Pewter) (bottom left)*

Fig. I:22 *Hand-formed box 'The Inner I', Frances Felton. (Courtesy of Shirley Charron) (top right)*

Fig. I:23 *Life Guard, Buckingham Pewter. Photo: Francis Thompson Studios Ltd) (bottom right)*

MALAYSIA

Malaysia today has a thriving industry which, in terms of the craft, can be regarded as relatively young, with the first pewter pieces, as distinct from those of pure tin, being produced by a young Chinese immigrant Yong Koon, just before the end of the nineteenth century. The majority of Malaysian pewter today is cast using traditional methods in a high tin alloy (up to 98%) – giving a slightly lighter colour. Little of this fine range of pewter has so far found its way to Europe, but it is widely distributed throughout the Far East.

JAPAN

Pewtercraft has been practised in Japan for over 300 years, mainly centred in the Kyoto, Osaka and Kagoshima regions. Much of the traditional pewterware produced is distinctive in having surface colouration in soft pastel shades, with delicate engraved designs showing to great effect.

In 1981 The Japan Pewterers Association was formed, incorporating 17 manufacturing companies with the aim of establishing standards for the craft similar to those of the Associations in Europe and the USA.

With Brazil and India also manufacturing a wide range of pewter articles, it can be seen that pewterware is being produced in every continent of a quality that is, in the main, well up to the high standards that were originally established by the craft guilds 500 years ago.

SUMMARY

Pewter is manufactured today in many countries often to the exacting standards laid down by the national trade associations established by the pewter manufacturers as a guarantee of the high quality of their products. The range and style of their pewter reflects national tastes, in some cases over hundreds of years.

It is to be hoped that these associations may be encouraged to look outwards with a view perhaps to developing reciprocal trading arrangements between pewterers of different nationalities. If this were to happen, we could all gain an opportunity to see and appreciate the enormous range of quality pewter that is currently being produced.

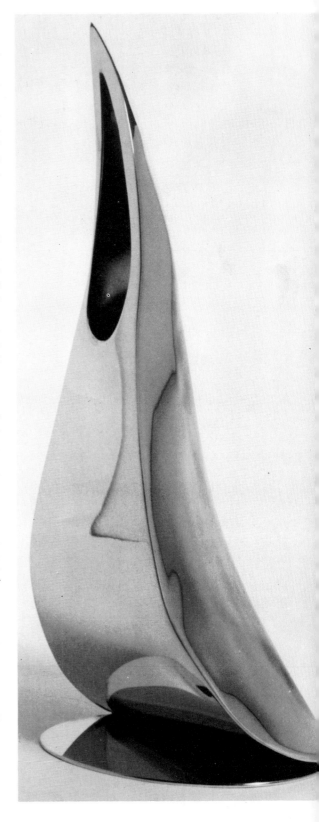

Fig. I:24 *Sculptured vase, Shirley Charron. (Courtesy of Shirley Charron)*

II The Metal

INTRODUCTION

Modern pewter is composed predominantly of tin (Sn) with small additions of antimony (Sb) and copper (Cu) to increase its strength.

Occasionally, other metals such as bismuth (Bu) are also added. In the past metal contained a high proportion of lead, which accounts for the confusion still around today regarding its definition and acceptance. There is no lead added to modern pewter and the impurity level is severely restricted by the relevant standards throughout the world. In the UK and Germany the level is limited to a maximum of 0.5% and in the USA to a maximum of 0.05%. Apart from its toxicity, lead has the effect of darkening the pewter and causing it to tarnish easily, which is the reason for the difference in appearance between old pewter and the modern non-tarnishing pewter.

The major constituent, tin, is produced from tin ore, the major sources of supply being Malaya, the Far East and Bolivia. Smaller sources are found elsewhere in the world, including the UK, which was a major source some two thousand years ago. Tin is completely non-toxic, melts at a relatively low temperature, 232°C (450°F), has very good fluidity when molten, has good formability, and readily forms alloys with other metals. It is a relatively soft metal, and it is for this reason that it is alloyed with other constituents before being used in the form of pewter.

The tin used as the basic constituent of pewter is very pure, ranging from 99% to 99.75% purity. The higher purity tin is called Standard Tin, and the lower purity tin is called Common Tin. For pewter, Standard Tin is used so as to limit the impurities, particularly lead.

ALLOYING

The most common alloying elements in pewter are antimony, which melts at 630°C (1,166°F), and copper, which melts at 1,083°C (1,981°F). Despite these wide differences in melting temperatures, there are no problems in alloying if the procedures are correctly carried out. The tin is melted first, and brought up to a temperature approaching 400°C (752°F) and the desired proportion of copper is then added. The copper is added in the form of thin sheet or foil to present the maximum surface area for wetting by the molten tin. This wetting action causes the copper to dissolve quickly and easily. The antimony can be added in lumps as these dissolve very easily once fully wetted by the molten tin. To assist in the wetting action, the copper and antimony can be dipped in a zinc chloride flux prior to entering the melting pot. Some stirring with a steel paddle is desirable to ensure that the alloying additions are well-dispersed throughout the melt, bearing in mind they are only a few percent of the total mix. For convenience and improved dispersion, master alloys are often used. These are commonly premix alloys of 50% tin and 50% antimony or 90% tin and 10% copper. Correct proportions of these are then added to a melt of pure tin to form the final alloy. It is important that the mix is accurately controlled both on quantities and temperature for repeatability. Once manufacturing procedures have been established in a pewter workshop, it is important that the supply of raw material is consistent from batch to batch, whether it be casting ingots or sheet materials. For this reason raw material suppliers have sophisticated laboratories and quality control procedures to ensure accuracy and consistency of their particular alloys.

The alloys are made up in large iron melting pots either gas-fired or electrically heated. After melting and thorough mixing, the alloy is cast into ingots for producing cast pewterware or slabs for subsequent rolling into sheets. The ingots for future casting are cast into moulds, so that each ingot is of handleable size around 10 kilos (22 lbs) and often segmented like a chocolate bar so that it can be cut or broken easily into smaller pieces. The slabs for rolling into sheet are cast into square or rectangular moulds, approximately 300 mm (12 in.) × 250 mm (10 in.) of 50 mm (2 in.) thickness.

Prior to casting into ingots or slabs, the alloy, which may have been at a temperature of near 400°C (752°F), is allowed to cool to approximately 300°C (572°F), which is around 50°C (90°F) above its melting point, before pouring. If it is poured in an overheated condition there may not be even dispersion in the alloy and the cast block will be coarse grained which will be detrimental to future work, particularly if the ingot or slab is to be rolled. Care must also be taken to ensure that no dross passes into the moulds and this is best done by pouring the metal from below its free surface. If a ladle is being used, then the surface of the melt must be skimmed of dross before ladling.

ROLLING

The slabs of pewter in their 'as cast form' will have a rough oxidised surface and the upper surface will have considerable shrinkage marks and depressions. The upper and lower surfaces are therefore machined off, on a slab milling machine which removes approximately 18 mm ($\frac{3}{8}$ in.) from each surface to leave a flat smooth finish. The cuttings are returned to the melting pot in strict proportion, up to a maximum of 10%. The slabs are then passed through banks of rolling mills which successively reduce the thickness. It is important that the rolls of these mills are polished to a high finish and every care must be taken to keep the sheet clean to avoid pressing dirt or other foreign substances into the surface. During the process of reducing the thickness of the sheet it is turned through 90° and rolling then continues in this direction. During the reduction process the pewter softens quite considerably from its original 'as cast' hardness. This is mainly due to a reduction in crystal size and distribution, caused by the rolling and reducing action. It has been found that this effect can be reduced by changing the direction of rolling part way through the process. The rolling and reduction continues until the desired sheet thickness is reached. Sheets are in fact rolled to specific thicknesses as ordered by the customer, but are generally in the range of 0.6 mm (0.025 in.) to 1.9 mm (0.075 in.). Foil is also produced on a special foiling machine, which not only reduces the sheet by rolling but also by stretching at the same time. This combined action of rolling and stretching gives a very accurately sized and formed foil. The foil is produced in 300 mm (12 in.) wide reels in two common thicknesses of 0.125

mm (0.005 in.) and 0.175 mm (0.007 in.). After rolling to desired thickness, the sheets are cut into standard or specified sizes and packed for transport.

Considerable care is taken in packing in order to protect the mirror finish surface. The pewter sheets are interleaved with heavy paper sheets and individual stacks are packed in wooden crates for complete protection. Alternatively, the rolled sheets are immediately stamped into blanks of convenient size and shape for subsequent manufacture of items such as tankards, bowls, etc. Shaped blanks and discs of various sizes are produced on a blanking press. The sheets are fed in by hand and the blanks are taken away individually spaced on a conveyor, again great care being taken not to damage the surface. Off-cuts from the sheets after blanking are returned to the melting pot.

REMELTING

Remelting of ingots for use in castings is relatively easy because of the low melting point of pewter alloys. No sophisticated equipment is required, and cast iron or welded steel vessels are suitable as melting pots. Small quantities can be melted directly in a ladle using a gas blow torch. The melting pot must of course be substantial enough to stand the weight of the molten alloy and for safety should be standing on a firm base. Any attack on the vessel by the molten metal is negligible particularly if the vessel is initially coated with iron oxide paint or a lime wash. Molten tin does not dissolve gas and the initial layer of tin oxide that forms on the melt does not dissolve into the bulk. In fact, once this film is formed it protects the molten metal underneath from further oxidisation. Flux need not be used in the melt though if a lot of re-work is used a flux will clean the metal and disperse the dross.

If a pot is allowed to go solid, then care must be taken with the re-melt. Bottom heat only can give rise to a dangerous situation where the bottom of the solid block melts and expands whilst the top is still solid and stuck to the walls of the pot. In this situation, the solid portion could be ejected quite violently. All-round side heating is preferable or alternatively a central hole could be melted out using a torch. Continuous re-melting is not generally too detrimental, though there is some evidence to suggest that with very high-quality and difficult castings it is preferable to use virgin metal.

DIFFERENT ALLOYS

A considerable amount of research has been carried out with regard to tin–antimony–copper alloys to determine the ideal alloys for use in the pewter industry. The overall situation is complex and demands a sound knowledge of metallurgy to appreciate it fully. Based both on practice and later research, it has been shown that the best alloys for pewterware are tin alloys containing from 4% to 8% antimony and from 0.5% to 2% copper. Within this range there are a number of standard alloys available in the UK, Europe and the USA. In addition, a number of pewter casters use their own traditional alloys which have been handed down from generation to generation. Most of these do in fact fall into the range quoted above, though some contain small quantities of bismuth or other metals such as nickel and silver.

The alloys fall into two main categories, casting alloys and sheet alloys. Without going too deeply into the metallurgy, the following explanation is given to help the pewtersmith, particularly the new ones, to understand the reasons for the different alloys.

Tin alone is too soft for normal work and some hardening is necessary, therefore an alloy is required. When an alloy is formed from two or more metals, the temperature at which the alloy melts is different from any of the individual melting temperatures. In addition to this, the temperature at which the alloy solidifies is not only different from any of the individual temperatures, but covers a range. This is because some of the constituent parts crystalise earlier than others whilst the mass is cooling. The temperature at which the alloy is fully solid is called the solidus and the temperature at which the alloy is fully liquid is called the liquidus. Depending upon the particular alloy, the temperature difference between the solidus and liquidus can be quite considerable. This difference is called the pasty phase, when the alloy is neither completely solid nor completely liquid. There are alloys with a particular mix of constituents that do in fact have no pasty phase and the transformation from liquid to soild occurs at one temperature. These are called eutectics, but this does not apply to the common pewter alloys, all of which have a pasty phase of some duration.

Either antimony or copper alone has the effect of hardening the tin when alloyed with it. Antimony alone has a small effect on the melting point of the tin and an addition of 10% antimony will only raise the liquidus temperature by about 15°C (27°F). Unfortunately, whilst this would give a satisfactory hardness, there is a problem with this amount of antimony staying in solution with the tin. During re-melt for casting, some of the antimony forms cuboids with the tin and these float to the surface of the melt. There is therefore less antimony in the bulk and the excess will tend to be skimmed off with the dross. Copper alone has a considerable effect on the melting temperature, 10% copper will raise the liquidus temperature by some 200°C (360°F). The copper also darkens the alloy so that it loses the white lustrous appearance. Copper is virtually insoluble in tin and forms a compound. Crystals of this compound are feathery and needle-shaped, show little tendency to segregate and form a sort of open sponge in the melt. If copper is added to a tin–antimony alloy, this sponge effect has the ability of trapping any tin–antimony cuboids, preventing segregation.

The above factors therefore lead to a compromise situation where relatively high proportions of antimony can be used with small amounts of copper to hold the antimony within the alloy, without the copper having too great effect on the melting point.

It is generally agreed that a good casting alloy should have a short pasty phase to give good sharp surfaces and ease of casting. This is common practice throughout the industrial casting industry on the majority of materials. Consequently, a good casting alloy for pewter is one with sufficient antimony for hardness and only sufficient copper to retain the antimony. One such material is Fry's J30, which is 92% tin, 7.5% antimony and 0.5% copper. This has a solidus of 240°C (464°F) and a liquidus of 255°C (491°F), giving a pasty phase of only 15°C (27°F).

For sheet material, the pasty phase is unimportant as it is not normally re-melted so more copper can be used as a hardener, provided it has no effect on colour. A typical sheet metal alloy is one with 92% tin, 6% antimony and 2% copper. This is harder than the cast alloy which helps compensate for the softening that takes place during rolling and reducing. The solidus of this material is 244°C (471°F) and the liquidus is 295°C (563°F), giving a long pasty phase of 51°C (92°F). This material is called Britannia metal as it falls within the range of the original Britannia metal alloys introduced towards the end of the eighteenth century.

Further studies have been carried out into the problem of pewter alloys softening during the rolling and reduction process and the addition of a small amount of bismuth has been found to improve the hardness. If there is any lead present by contamination there is a danger of a bismuth-containing alloy to crack whilst being worked. Consequently, these alloys are not used to a great extent, particularly if re-work or scrap pewter has to be used, for the risk of lead contamination would increase due to solder inclusions. It has also been shown that a heat treatment process after rolling or working can recover most of the lost hardness. The problem is that the temperature needs to be around 200°C (392°F), which really makes the process impracticable for finished work, as this temperature is above or very close to the melting points of solders used in assembly.

A recent innovation by the International Tin Research Institute, which may have potential in the pewter industry, is the introduction of a composite material. This is a sheet of copper on to which is bonded a sheet of pewter, either on to one side or both. The bond is permanent, and the sandwich has the appearance of pewter with the strength of the copper and can be satisfactorily spun to simple forms.

CONCLUSION

There is general agreement in the pewter industry that Britannia metal, or a similar alloy, is best for sheetwork. There is no general agreement on casting alloys, and opinions and practice vary considerably. It is probably these differences of practice that make agreement impossible, as there are so many variables in casting, such as melt temperature, pour temperature, ingate size and shape, mould materials, cooling rates, etc. that the whole process becomes a technique which has been handed down or learned by constant practice. Consequently, it is found that some casters use an alloy similar to Britannia metal with a long pasty phase, whilst at the other end of the range, some use an alloy that contains only 1% copper and 1% antimony and is therefore 98% tin.

For the pewtersmith new to casting it would seem prudent to use an alloy that is specifically produced for casting and purchased from a major supplier. This would ensure consistency for at least one of the elements in the casting process.

III Design and Application

DESIGNING PEWTERWARE

The approach to design must be one of freedom and not restricted by rules. There are of course guidelines which can be followed, and there are practical restrictions with regard to the material being used. The correct balance of these factors with the instinctive imagination of the craftsmen forms the basis of good design.

Pewterware on the market today can be classified under three main headings, reproduction, traditional and modern. These classifications are not really explicit, as what is modern today is historic in the future. An analysis of the function, the surroundings and environment of the age in which a particular article was first made give an insight into the mind of the designer at that time. It is this analysis which will give the craftsman some guidelines as to the design of the article he is about to produce.

If the piece is to be designed for a particular setting, then that setting must influence the design. If the piece is to be purely functional, then that must be the overriding influence.

For a historical setting a study of period pieces by photographs or physical examination will give a basis for a design. The physical examination by handling and touch give a much greater insight into the design, for weight and balance and the feel of form are an integral part of the design.

Whilst historical accuracy may be necessary to suit the setting or requirement, there is still scope for the individual to exert his or her own influence on the design. Subtle changes to line and proportion, based on the designer's own interpretation, give characteristics to the article so that it is in keeping with the spirit of the age, rather than a reproduction.

It is essential to design within the limitations of

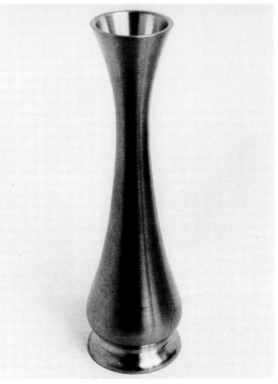

Fig. III:1 *Traditional cast pieces, A. E. Williams.*

Fig. III:2 *Modern cast vase, Abbey Pewter Ltd.*

the material. These limitations must however be those determined by the craftsman. Like all crafts, there is a tendency for limitations to be set by hearsay, and whilst the craftsman should take note, he or she should not be afraid to try out a process or technique even if it means the possibility of scrapping some material. There are some obvious limitations with pewter because of its inherent softness. Sharp edges, or piercing and tracing, as used on precious metals such as silver and gold, are not really practical in the design of pewterware. Large flat surfaces are also impractical, unless very heavy gauges are used. There are also limitations on the functional use of articles because of the low melting point and therefore its use on hot plates or stoves.

On the other hand, the ease of working the material makes it possible to give added strength by incorporating into the design curved or domed surfaces. The ease with which it can be joined, almost invisibly, by solder means that relatively complex and pleasing shapes can be designed and produced of an item consisting of a number of parts.

The effects of light and shade have as great an effect on the design as the line and form. The ease with which pewter can be finished to a wide range of appearances from highly polished through satin finishes to textured surfaces has considerable influence on the design. Two pieces of identical form look quite different with different surface finishes. It is a worthwhile experiment to produce or obtain two identical pieces and give them different surface finishes. The effect of light and shade on the form will be shown quite dramatically by the experiment, and this will be an aid to future design.

The method of manufacture must be borne in mind during the initial design, as this is of considerable consequence. Spunware, by the very nature of the process, must be circular and its form should be of free-flowing curves, if curves are used. Sharp changes of direction are difficult in spunware, so a number of pieces may have to be soldered together. The design will again be influenced by the practical considerations of the joint positions.

In designing castware, care must be taken with thin sections, sharp edges and re-entrant angles, all of which are difficult or noncompatible with the process.

Similarly with handwork the limitations on the amount of forming, stretching or compression will affect the design.

Fig. III:3 *Spun candlestick, PMC Ltd, Sheffield.*

Fig. III:4 *Prototype modern designs, Daalderop B.V.*

An interesting and useful exercise for the designer/craftsman is to take three pieces of work, handformed, spun and cast. Then compare them with each other and attempt to determine how, or if, each piece could be produced by using one of the other processes. This will show quite clearly the limitations of each particular method of manufacture.

Decoration as part of the design is a difficult subject. If an object is designed purely from the functional approach, then decoration becomes almost illogical. Surface decoration should be used sparingly and where possible should grow out of the function. It can be used to draw attention to some particular part of the design or to add interest to a large open area. It can also be used as part of the manufacturing process such as, for example, a decorated strengthening ring around the top of a bowl. Engraved lines can be used to hide a soldered joint or to emphasise a bulge or curve.

In all cases, the decoration should conform to the design and be of low relief rather than high relief. This is particularly true of functional items which are liable to be in constant use, as high relief work is very easily worn away and difficult to clean.

Decoration must be built into the original design concept and not be added on afterwards. In this particularly difficult area, a useful phrase to remember is 'If in doubt – leave it out'.

A study of pewterware throughout the world does also show up some national traditions and tendencies. These, naturally, have an influence on the designer. The individual craftsman can, by a study of these characteristics, develop an international approach in combination with an individual approach.

Whilst there is modern work being produced in all countries, there is still a considerable demand for pewterware traditional to that country. The designer for a commercial pewter company therefore has some limitations imposed by the market. In order to introduce new products, the traditional demands of the market must be borne in mind yet at the same time products should be designed that influence the market.

Not only are designs traditional to respective countries, but also the method of manufacture. German pewter tends to be heavy, ornate and cast, whilst in the USA the majority of work is spun and based on early colonial designs. Malayan pewterware is mainly cast, but of clean-flowing, plain design, mostly satin finished. France and Belgium produce mainly traditional cast items, whilst in the UK there is a reasonable mixture of spunware and castware,

both in traditional and modern design. There is a growing pewter industry in Australia, and also in Japan. The Japanese pewter design tends to follow the delicacy and finish of its other arts and crafts, and its tradition of lacquered work is carried through into its pewter in the form of coloured decoration.

When designing pewterware, other materials should not be ignored. The white sheen and high polish obtainable with pewter can give very attractive associations with wood, glass and coloured enamels.

There is no doubt that top-rate designers, like top-rate craftsmen, have flair as well as knowledge, but this should not deter the craftsman from breaking new ground. The basic elements of design and the limitations of the materials can be learned. A study and analysis of existing designs will give an understanding and appreciation of line and form. With this background and freedom of thought, good designs can be produced.

A sketch book should always be available in the workshop to make design sketches and notes as and when required. The most suitable pad is one with squared paper as this makes it much easier to draw

Fig. III:5 *Examples of German cast pewter, Stephan Grenningloh.*

or copy profiles. Apart from a few major dimensions, it is often possible to work direct from these sketches.

WORKING DRAWINGS

An understanding of the basic procedures of technical drawing and the basics of practical geometry is all that is required in the pewter workshop. Unlike engineering practice, it is rare for pewter work to be made to precise dimensions, fits or even initial shapes. However, there is a need for drawings with regard to developed shapes and sometimes for original pieces. The latter is particularly true for complex designs or pieces that are complicated to make and, of course, if a piece of work is commissioned.

Equipment

A simple drawing board and T-square will suffice as opposed to a professional drafting board, though if one is available it is more convenient to use. Two set squares, one 45° and one 60° of 20 cm (8 in.) side are suitable. An adjustable set square is a very useful addition if it can be afforded, as it does speed up the work when other angles are involved. A protractor, a clearly marked rule in centimetres and inches, a good eraser and two or three good-quality drawing pencils are also required. The pencils should be of grade 3H for construction lines and H or HB for lining in. Two pairs of pencil compasses, one large and one small, will complete the basic equipment. Other drawing aids, such as French curves and geometric shapes are useful for drawing in curved lines, but are not essential. If difficulty is encountered with drawing curved lines freehand then a very useful device is a Helix-E-Curve which is a length of flexible plastic that can be formed into

Fig. III:6 *Showing the use of ceramics in conjunction with pewter, Tether Manufacturing Ltd. (above)*

Fig. III:7 *Original design work and first-off model, Selangor Pewter Co. (Photo – Selangor Pewter Co.) (opposite)*

curved shapes which can be followed with a pencil. The modern technique is to draw directly on to tracing paper so that prints can be taken off, but this would be rarely needed in a pewtershop. As most of the drawing in the pewtershop will be developments, it is preferable to do these on good-quality cartridge paper or thin card, and cut them out and use them as templates. Usually the amount of construction line work extends way beyond the finished development and, in order to do this on a piece of pewter, a large sheet would be required. Furthermore, the less lines there are on the pewter the better, as they only have to be polished off. It is also quite common to do repeat work in the pewtershop, so the paper or card template can save a lot of repeat drawing.

Concepts and developments

The majority of pewter work consists of cylindrical or conical shapes or slight variations on these themes, so once these developments and a few other basic concepts have been mastered, there should be little difficulty in producing them.

Circles

To draw a circle or a curve through three points A, B and C, bisect AB and BC and the centre will be where the bisectors cross.

Ellipse

An ellipse has two axes, the major axis and the minor axis. There are a number of ways of drawing an ellipse, but the simplest method, which avoids a number of construction lines, is as follows. Draw the

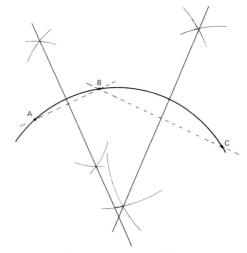

Diag. III:1   *Showing construction to find the centre of a curve to pass through three points.*

major axis and bisect it with the minor axis and extend it beyond its exact length. Take a thin strip of card and mark on it half the length of the major axis AC. From A mark off point B equal to half the length of the minor axis. By moving the trammel so that point B always remains on the major axis and point C always remains on the minor axis or its extension, point A will be a point on the ellipse. As the trammel is moved, point A is marked on the paper as a pencil point. The points are then joined up freehand or by using a flexi-curve to draw the ellipse.

Parabola

Parabolic shapes give a pleasing form for goblets or vases and in order to turn a chuck for spinning a template is required to get the correct curve. Having decided on the diameter or width and the height, the construction is quite straightforward.

Draw a rectangle ABCD to the desired dimensions. Draw a vertical centre line EF. Divide the vertical sides AC and BD into four or five equal parts and number them. Divide CF and FD into a similar number of parts and draw vertical lines also numbered. Now draw lines from E to each of the numbered points on AC and BD. Where lines of the same number cross is a point on the parabola. Join the points either freehand or with the flexi-curve to complete the curve. A template can then be cut to use on spun- or hand-formed work.

Hexagons and octagons

Polygonal shapes are attractive for tobacco jars and vases, the hexagon and octagon being most common.

Having determined the distance across the flats, the construction is simple using the standard set squares.

Draw a circle of diameter equal to the distance

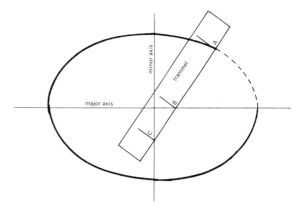

Diag. III:2   *Showing construction of an ellipse using the trammel method.*

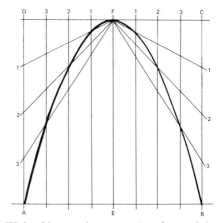

Diag. III:3   *Showing the construction of a parabola.*

across the flats. For a hexagon draw a vertical tangent each side of the circle. Then using the 30° side of a 60/30 set square, draw four more tangents to complete the hexagon.

For the octagon, draw two vertical tangents and two horizontal. Then draw four more using the 45° set square to complete the octagon. The lengths of the sides can now be measured from the drawing for the development.

Irregular curves

During the initial design of a vessel it is common for the shape to be a series of curves, either regular or irregular, merging into each other. It is relatively easy to draw one side of the profile, but a little more difficult to draw the other side to match. In order to do this, a process of offset projection is used.

Set up a centre line and, having determined the various diameters, draw the desired outline on one side using half the final diametrical dimension. Divide the centre line into a number of spaces – these do not necessarily have to be equal. Draw horizontal lines through these points of sufficient length to cover the required diameters. Where each horizontal line cuts the profile line, step this dimension off on the opposite side. This will give a number of points, which when joined up will repeat the profile on the opposite side. Templates can be made from this drawing to assist in the manufacture of the piece.

Enlargement or reduction of drawings

In order to perfect or design detail it is sometimes necessary to produce the drawing to a scale larger than the actual finished piece. You may also need to produce a copy smaller than the original. If the original is relatively simple, then a smaller copy can be made simply by reducing the dimensions to suit. For irregular curved profiles, dimensions are often difficult or complex to determine.

In order to produce a copy of smaller or larger dimensions, the simplest method is to use a grid. A square grid of an easily divided dimension is drawn over and around the original drawing or sketch. Another grid is than drawn to the reduced or enlarged scale. Points are then made on the second grid to correspond to points on the original grid, relative to the profile. The points on the second grid are then joined up to give a scale reproduction of the original. Alternatively, relatively inexpensive pantographs are available from drawing office supply shops.

Surface developments

In order to produce a piece of work to a drawing from a flat sheet of pewter, a pattern must be determined so that it will roll up or form the required

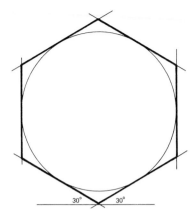

Diag. III:4   *Showing the construction of a hexagon around a circle.*

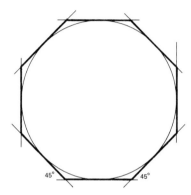

Diag. III:5   *Showing construction of an octagon around a circle.*

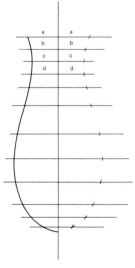

Diag. III:6   *Showing method of offset projection to repeat an irregular profile.*

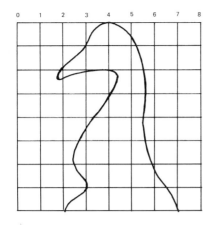

Diag. III:7 *Showing method of enlargement/reduction of an irregular shape.*

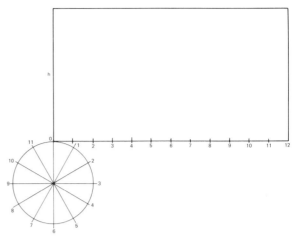

Diag. III:8 *Development of a cylinder.*

shape. The original drawing or profile of the object must therefore be developed into a flat pattern.

The most common developments in the pewter-shops are those of conical shapes and cylindrical shapes, though sometimes others are required. The techniques, however, are similar.

Cylinder development

This will develop into a rectangle and may be done theoretically or by practical drawing. The theoretical process is to draw a rectangle of height equal to that of the desired cylinder and length equal to 3.141 × the diameter of the cylinder. The practical method is to draw a circle equal in diameter to that of the desired cylinder. The length is determined by setting a pair of dividers or compasses to equal 1/12 of the circumference of the circle and stepping this out 12 times. Other prisms such as square hexagonal and octagonal are developed in a similar manner.

Conical development

This is the most common development used by the pewtersmith, though rarely a complete cone. It is more usual to develop a frustum of a cone for items such as tankards.

The elevation of the frustum is drawn and the two sides extended until they intersect. Using this point as a centre, arcs are drawn from the bottom and top of the frustum. A circle equal to the diameter of the bottom is drawn and divided into 12 parts with the 60/30 set square. Using the dividers or compasses, one of these divisions is stepped off 12 times around the lower arc. A line is drawn from the last point to the centre of the arcs, thus completing the development.

Pyramids or frustums of pyramids are developed in a similar manner.

The major problem with developing frustums,

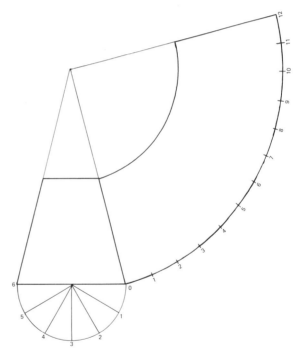

Diag. III:9 *Development of frustum of a cone.*

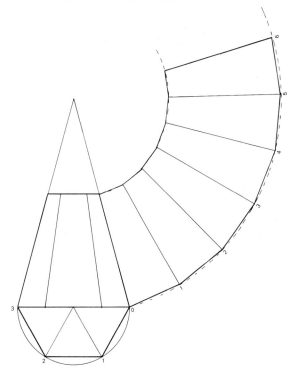

Diag. III:10   *Development of frustum of a hexagonal pyramid.*

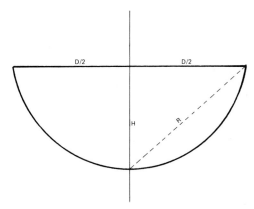

Diag. III:11   *Showing method of construction to determine diameter of flat sheet to produce a bowl.*

common in the pewtershop, is the length of the radius of the arc. The angles of the sides of a tankard for example are relatively shallow and when these sides are extended, it can be several feet before they intersect. This means that quite often the layout takes place on the floor as the bench or drawing board is too small. To cope with such a large radii, a length of wood is required, fitted with two trammel heads. Alternatively, small holes can be drilled to suit the three points. A nail can act as a pivot point for the centre, and a pencil point through the other two holes will mark out the arcs.

Hollowed articles

To obtain the exact shape of a sheet in the flat for an article whose surface has a double curvature is generally almost impossible. In practice, however, very good approximations can be found. A good guide is to work on equal surface areas, on the assumption that the thickness of the sheet is not changed in the work progress. On this basis, if the finished article is to be, for example, a hemispherical bowl, then the starting point must be a flat circular disc of surface area equal to that of the hemisphere. It can be shown mathematically that the diameter of the flat disc is equal to the diameter of the hemispherical bowl divided by 0.7, that is

$$\text{Dia. of disc} = \frac{\text{Dia. of bowl}}{0.7}.$$

Even if the bowl is not a perfect hemisphere, this formula will give a reasonable approximation for raised or spun work. The radius of the flat disc may also be found graphically by setting out a right-angled triangle with one side being equal to the designed depth, the other being equal to half the diameter of the bowl. The hypotenuse of this triangle is equal to the radius of the flat disc.

Complex developments

The layout of more complex developments is beyond the scope of this book as it is a subject in itself. A text book on sheet and metal platework will give many examples and is a useful book to have in the workshop.

For items such as spouts, handles and bases, it is possible to make up models in wax or plasticine to get the correct shape and fit. From these models, paper patterns can be made and folded up and then when correct, can be used as templates to cut the pewter sheet. Until experience is gained it is a good idea to cut a paper pattern first to confirm the development before cutting a sheet of pewter.

IV Workshop Tools and Equipment

WORKSHOP

In order to practice the craft of the pewtersmith some form of workshop is essential. The size is, of course, dependent upon individual circumstances, whether it be for an amateur craftsman, a professional craftsman, a small group of craftsmen or a large company. In addition to these options there are others concerned with the craft itself. There is a tendency for the pewter industry to segregate into two distinct groups, the casters and the spinners, with the consequent differing requirements. Hand-forming is a third group, which can be on its own or more closely linked with spinning than with casting. In order therefore to cover the basic requirements of the craft, a workshop suitable for a professional craftsman wishing to cover the majority of processes will be described.

For the single craftsman, an ideal workshop can be built up in an area the size of a single car garage, say 3 m × 6 m (10 ft × 20 ft). The layout should be designed to suit the flow of work, so that the amount of walking to and fro, for tools and equipment, is limited. The main workbench should be sited under a window if possible, so that work can be done under natural light as often as possible. The work areas should be grouped for convenience and work flow. For example, soldering and casting together, buffing and polishing together and away from the work bench, machinery together to reduce the amount of electrical installation required. Adequate storage should be provided for the specific equipment and tools for each area. Lighting should be of a relatively high level – fluorescent tubes give very good shadowless light.

Ventilation is desirable in the casting and soldering area, and the buffing and polishing area, and wall extractor fans are ideal for this purpose. Wherever possible, tools and equipment should be stored on shelves or in cupboards rather than in boxes on the floor, so that the floor can be easily swept. There is always a danger of fire in any workshop, so a good fire extinguisher should be mounted in a convenient position and a bucket of water should always be available. Water must never be used on an electrical fire, so the fire extinguisher should be of a type suitable for electrical fires as well as others. A first aid box should always be available in the workshop. If the floor of the workshop is concrete then it should be sealed with a proprietory cement sealer, to prevent it from dusting up during sweeping. Some form of heating is also desirable during the winter months, as it is impossible to turn out good work when shivering with the cold. Protective clothing should always be worn in

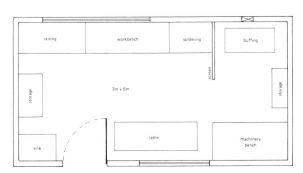

Diag. IV:1 *Workshop layout.*

the workshop. A complete coverall or boiler suit is to be preferred to the warehouse type of coat which can catch upon moving equipment. Strong stout shoes or boots should always be worn as there is always the danger of dropping something heavy or sharp or both.

TOOLS AND EQUIPMENT

Benches
The basic requirement is a good work bench which should be strong and sturdy with a good hardwood top. Dimensions should be approximately 200 cm × 60 cm (6 ft × 2 ft) and 75 cm high (2 ft 6 in.). A pin or peg should be fitted to the bench so that it protrudes over the edge of the bench. This is a piece of hardwood, wedge-shaped, and sometimes with a V cut in it, that is used to support work for filing or sawing. The peg can be fitted with a clamp or a bolt so that it can be moved out of the way. Benches can be made up, or purchased ready made, either in plain form or as a jewellers' bench. The jewellers' bench has a semi-circular cut out and a peg already fitted. They also have fittings for blow torches and air blowers or gas containers.

Vices
The next essential is a good vice of adequate size. A wide range of vices is available, and as well as a good engineers' or mechanics' vice, a smaller vice should also be fitted for small delicate work. When mounting the vice on the bench it is important that the face of the back jaw sits beyond the front edge of the bench so that long work or sheets can be hung below the vice. Fibre vice jaws or grips should be available for use on the vice to prevent marking the work.

Bench drill
Whilst it is possible to use a hand drill or an electric drill for most of the work, a small powered bench drill is a good investment. For the small workshop a drill with a chuck of 18 cm ($\frac{3}{8}$ in.) capacity with a $\frac{1}{4}$ HP motor is ideal. A pair of V-blocks and a drilling machine vice are also useful, as well as sets of drills in imperial and metric sizes. Small pieces of flat hardwood should always be available when drilling sheet so that the drill does not pass through and damage the table.

Bench grinder
For sharpening drills, scribers and other tools a

Fig. IV:1 *Showing engineers' vice, small subsidiary vice and jewellers' peg.*

Fig. IV:2 *Bench drill with drills, vee blocks and vice.*

Fig. IV:3 *Bench grinder and polishing spindle.*

Fig. IV:4 *Engineers' lathe.*

small bench grinder is required. A $\frac{1}{4}$ HP unit fitted with 125 mm diameter (5 in.) grinding wheels is adequate for the small workshop. Grinding wheels of various grit size are available and in various diameters. It is important to fit wheels as recommended by the manufacturer with regard to the bore and the diameter of the clamping washer. In order to economise in this area, the bench grinder can also serve as the polishing motor by using a polishing spindle on one end and the grinding wheel on the other.

Polishing motor

This should ideally be a double-ended unit, and for the small workshop a $\frac{1}{2}$ HP machine is adequate. For the larger workshop, machines up to 5 HP are available. The ideal speed is 2,800 rpm for general use and the cutting speed can be varied by using mops or brushes of different diameters. Some form of shield or part cover should be provided to prevent polish and dust being thrown around during the polishing operation. Polishing mops, brushes and polishers should be stored adjacent to the machine. A peg board is a convenient way of storing mops. In addition to the fixed polishing motor, a flexible drive unit is a useful item in the workshop.

Lathe

If the pewtersmith wishes to cover a reasonable range of work, some form of lathe is desirable. There are three types of lathes, an engineers' lathe, a wood-turning lathe and a spinning lathe, that can be used. If it is intended to carry out a lot of spinning work, then a lathe designed specifically for the job should be provided. This will also be suitable for turning wood for mandrels and stakes and for hand-turning pewter castings. An engineers' lathe can be used for light and small spinnings, wood turning and for turning castings, but really only suitable for the latter. For the small workshop, the wood-turning lathe is a very good compromise. It will turn wooden mandrels, stakes or chucks for use in hand work or spinning. Using metal-cutting hand tools, it will turn or machine pewter castings. It is also adequate for lightweight, medium-sized spinning as it is similar in construction to a spinning lathe, though with generally lighter service bearings.

If a lathe is to be installed, it is essential to ensure that the electrical wiring and power supply is adequate and the services of a qualified electrical installer should be used.

Home-made machinery

For the small workshop it is possible to build such items as a grinder, polisher and even a simple light-weight lathe. The Picador Engineering Co. Ltd produce a very wide range of pulleys, bearings, shafts, belts and accessories from which it is possible to build up simple machines. Some engineering knowledge is required, but many items come in the form of shafts already threaded and mounted in bearings so that they can be mounted on wooden or metal bases. Secondhand motors, as used in washing machines, are fairly easy to come by and small machines can be built up relatively easily and cheaply.

Soldering bench

Soldering can take place on the workbench or in a separate area. A metal tool cabinet or old kitchen cabinet makes a useful compact unit for soldering and storage. A metal top should be provided with some firebrick surround. The cupboard can be used for storing torches, gas cylinders, solder fluxes, etc. Brazing hearths are commercially available, and they can be used as a compact soldering area. A small turntable is also useful and can be purchased ready made. Alternatively, one can easily be made up from a piece of plate attached to a shaft of 18 mm ($\frac{3}{4}$ in.) diameter by 50 mm (2 in.) long. The shaft is supported in two ball races let into a block of wood. A thin asbestos mat, a domestic cooking mat, not builders' asbestos sheet, placed on the turntable gives adequate protection and support during soldering.

Torches

The torch is probably one of the most important tools in the pewter workshop and care should be taken in choosing one that is adequate for the purpose. Torches can be fired by natural gas or bottled gas and are either self-blowing or require a source of low-pressure, compressed air.

Natural gas has replaced coal gas in many countries and it is important to ensure that the torch is designed for natural gas, as this has different characteristics from coal gas. Natural gas is hotter than coal gas and it is also cleaner, as it is almost devoid of undesirable sulphur compounds. If a natural gas torch with an air blower is installed, the installation must be approved by the local Gas Board who will require a flow back valve to be fitted between the torch and the gas meter and possibly other safety precautions.

Bottle gas or LP gas is a high-grade clean gas consisting of two varieties, propane and butane or a mixture of both. Propane is most used for heating tools, in workshops and for outdoor use. Butane is also in common use but needs to be used at room temperature for maximum efficiency as it does not perform satisfactorily at temperatures below 5°C (41°F). Propane will work at temperatures well below freezing point, so for an unheated workshop or on cold mornings, propane is to be preferred.

As with all gas appliances safety precautions must be taken. Adequate ventilation is required when

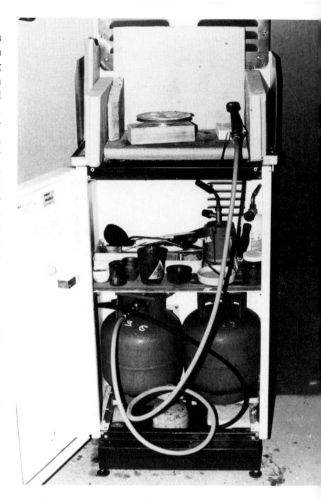

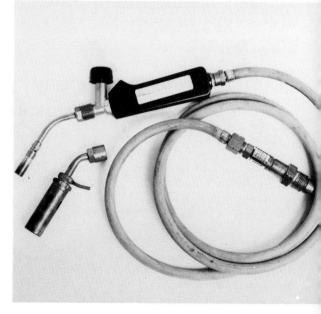

Fig. IV:5 *Soldering bench, cabinet and home-made turntable.*

Fig. IV:6 *Sievert torch for propane gas with needle flame and large burners.*

appliances are in use. Hoses and joints should be checked regularly for leaks. All gases have a distinctive odour which is deliberately put into the gas as a means of detecting leaks. Never use a naked flame when leaks are suspected. Soapy water applied to the joints with a brush will show leaks very readily with the continuous formation of bubbles. The extra surface tension of soapy water makes it preferable to plain water for this checking operation. After use, turn off the gas at the main cock or bottle before turning off the torch so that no gas is left in the hoses. Spare cylinders should be stored safely away from cylinders in use. LP gas is heavier than air and in the event of a leak, builds up from the floor. If a workshop has been closed and unused for some time it is advisable to leave the door open for a few minutes before use.

Torches are normally supplied with hoses and fittings and it is essential to use the fitting supplied as often these have regulators or cut-off devices built into them and are designed to suit the operation of the particular torch. A whole range of nozzles or burners are available for each torch, though for the pewter workshop two are usually sufficient. For soldering, the needle flame or very fine flame burner is required. For melting, one of the larger nozzles or burners is required.

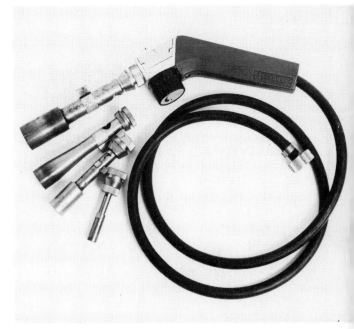

There are a number of torches on the market such as Alcosa and Flamefast that use natural gas, or LP gas, and air at pressures ranging from $\frac{3}{4}$ psig (50 mb) to 15 psig (1,000 mb). The manufacturers' leaflets set out the capacities and suitability of each torch, so it is relatively easy to select a suitable torch. For torches that do not require air supply, the range offered by Primus-Sievert and Gaz give the craftsman a wide choice. The Sievert torch has a particular fine needle flame burner as well as larger burners.

In addition to piped torches, both companies and others offer small torches using disposable gas cartridges. These also have a range of burners and, for the small workshop, give adequate performance. The disposable cartridges are normally butane, but a recent introduction by Primus-Sievert is a cartridge containing a 40/60 mix of propane and butane which in conjunction with a fine flame burner gives a very economical and powerful torch.

For very fine work miniature torches are also available, examples being the Micro flame range, the

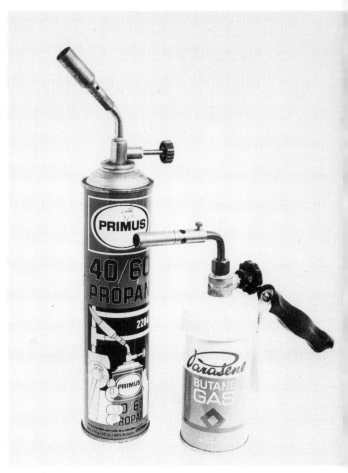

Fig. IV:7 *Gaz torch for butane with range of burners.*

Fig. IV:8 *Examples of small portable torches with needle flame burners.*

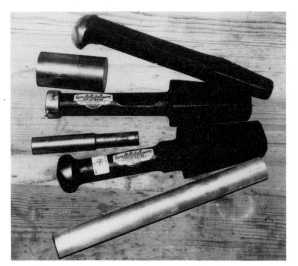

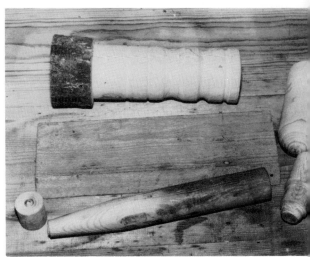

Flaminaire and a bench model by Flamefast.

Whilst all of the torches mentioned are excellent, the choice becomes somewhat personal with regard to balance, feel, valve action, etc. and before purchase time should be spent in viewing and handling and studying the literature.

Casting

The basic requirement for pewter casting is some form of melting pot and ladles. For occasional small casting the pewter can be melted directly in the ladle using a torch with a larger burner. For the small workshop a plumbers' lead melting pot mounted on a gas burner is quite adequate. If a considerable amount of casting is to be undertaken, then more sophisticated melting pots of larger capacity are also available. Many of the companies supplying torches also have a range of melting pots and ladles.

Raising and forming

For hand-forming pewter a number of specialised tools or forms are required. Forming blocks for bowls or shallow trays are easily made from blocks of hardwood, or sections of tree trunks, either turned out on the lathe or hand-carved. For finishing and final work, various shaped pieces of metal or hardwood are required. These are known as stakes and consist of a hard metal polished head welded to a wrought-iron shank. The shape of the head is designed to suit the particular requirement of the shape to be formed. Over the years a number of standard shapes and sizes have evolved, and a complete range of some thirty or more is available. These need only be purchased as required, but initially a half-moon stake, a round-head stake and a round-bottom stake form a good basis. For occasional use wooden shapes can be turned on the

Fig. IV:9   *A selection of stakes and formers: round head (lower), bottoming (centre), half moon (upper).*

Fig. IV:10   *Various home-made wooden stakes and formers.*

lathe or carved out. Lengths of metal shafting of various diameters are required for forming cylinders and flattening seams. Odd lengths of standard stock can be obtained from a metal merchant or a scrapyard.

The stakes can be held in a vice or in a special support. A special socket is available that fits into a bench top so that the stakes are held firmly and at a good working height. One or two leather sandbags are extremely useful for forming and also for supporting work during other operations. Sandbags are available through jewellery equipment suppliers, though it is possible to make them from suitably sized old leather handbags packed tight with sand in a plastic bag.

Each time a new stake or wooden form is made it should be stored away after use. In a short while a large collection of shapes and sizes will then be available to cope with future work.

HAND TOOLS

Like the equipment, some basic items are required initially, but others can be bought or made as required until eventually a large collection is built up and available.

Measuring and layout tools

30 cm (12 in.) and 15 cm (6 in.) rules graduated in inches and millimetres

2 m (6 ft) tape measure graduated in inches and millimetres

Fig. IV:11 *Leather sandbag made up from an old leather bag.*

Fig. IV:12 *Cutting tools – saws, wire cutters and snips.*

Scriber and pencil
Centre punch
15 cm (9 in.) engineers' square
Compasses for marking scribed lines
Protractor
Set squares, 45° and 60°
Depth gauge
Vernier or micrometer, to measure plate thickness
Inside calipers
Outside calipers
Angle gauge

When marking out on pewter a scriber should only be used on cutting lines, as scriber lines are very difficult to remove on finished work. All other lines should be marked out in pencil which can be easily wiped off.

Cutting tools
30 cm (12 in.) hacksaw with fine blades
Junior hacksaw with fine tooth blades
Junior hacksaw with circular profiling blade
Jewellers' saw with fine tooth blade
Tinman's snips – straight

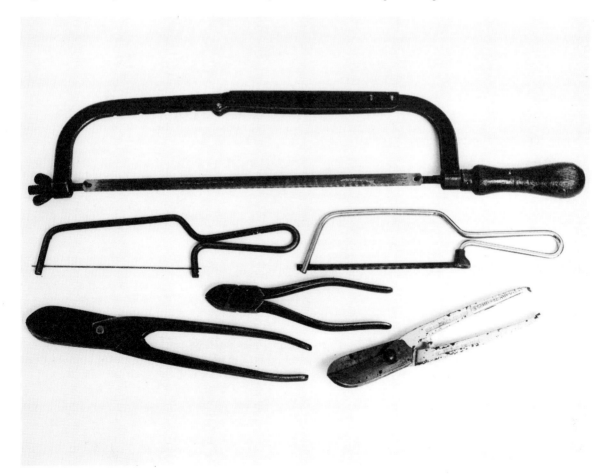

Tinman's snips – curved
Side cutters – for cutting wire and solder
Sheet saw for cutting large sheets
Cutting knife with replaceable blades
Scrapers

The blades for hacksaws should have teeth of very fine pitch as the major use will be on pewter sheet. For ease of sawing there should always be two teeth in contact with the metal. The profile blade is an extremely useful tool for both external and internal profiles as it cuts in all directions and as it has teeth like a file, further filing is minimised. The sheet saw, though a little expensive, is a lot easier to use than snips for cutting large sheets and does not roll up the cut edges. The tinman's snips should be of good quality and two pairs are required, a straight pair for cutting straight lines and a curved pair for curved or profiled lines.

Files

There are a considerable number of shapes and sizes of files in different cuts. The three basic cuts or teeth form are Bastard, Second and Smooth. Most of the filing work on pewter is trimming and clean-

Fig. IV:13 *Typical set of files and file card.*

Fig. IV:14 *A selection of hammers: engineers ball pein (top), repoussé, planishing: ball and flat, planishing: flat, raising (bottom). (opposite)*

ing joints so only a few files are required in the basic tool kit. Others can be added as the work demands. One essential item is a file card or brush, which consists of many hundreds of steel wires mounted on a block, used for cleaning swarf from the file. Pewter being soft tends to clog files very easily, so they should be cleaned regularly during use. A file should never be used without a handle as the unsheathed tang can cause severe injury to the hand should the file catch up and snag. In use the full length of the file should be used with pressure being applied on the forward stroke and released on the return. A useful basic set of files is as follows:

Flat 20 cm (8 in.) bastard cut and
smooth cut
Flat 15 cm (6 in.) smooth cut
Half round 20 cm (8 in.) bastard cut and smooth cut

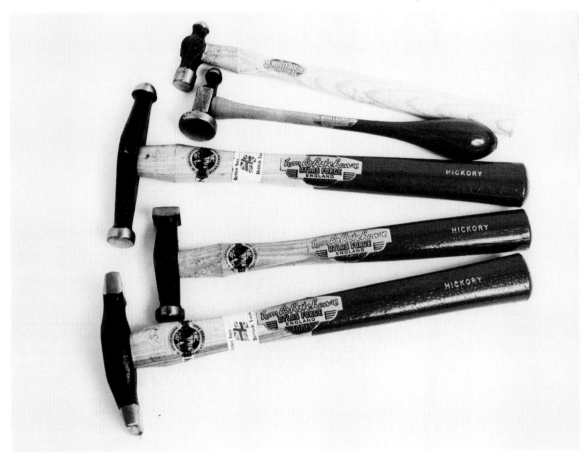

Half round 15 cm (6 in.) smooth cut
Round 20 cm (8 in.) second cut
Round 15 cm (6 in.) smooth .
Square 20 cm (8 in.) second cut
Square 15 cm (6 in.) smooth

In addition to the engineers' files above, a set of needle files of various shapes, 10 or 12 to a set, will cope with most work in the pewtershop.

Abrasives

Apart from the finishing and polishing compounds which are discussed later (see pp. 135–38), other abrasives should be included in the basic tool kit.

Emery cloth comes in various grades and sheet sizes, or strip wound as a reel. Only cloth-backed material should be purchased, as the paper-backed variety is not very substantial and whilst cheaper initially is more expensive in the long term. A few sheets of silicone carbide paper, known as Wet and Dry, in the finer grades should also be provided. Flexible plastic blocks with silicone carbide firmly attached or impregnated are available and are very convenient to hold and use. Worn strips should not be thrown away, as these are ideal for final polishing

and finishing, especially with a coating from a stick of chalk. One or two brass wire brushes should be provided as these are very good for polishing and finishing castings. Small brushes sold for cleaning suede shoes are ideal for this purpose. A packet of fine steel wire wool should also be provided.

Hammers

For beaten work, a range of hammers is available, often under the name of silversmiths' and art metal hammers. An initial set could be as follows:
115 g (4 oz) ball pein engineers' hammer for general use
140 g (5 oz) round and square-faced planishing hammer
256 g (9 oz) raising hammer
230 g (8 oz) ball and flat-face planishing hammer
115 g (4 oz) repoussé hammer – for repoussé and chasing punches

The surface of the faces of these hammers should always be kept clean and polished, and the hammers should be put away in a box or rack when not in use.

Fig. IV:15   *A selection of mallets: pear-shaped wood (top), flat-faced plastic (centre), soft-faced set of four (bottom).*

Miscellaneous tools and equipment

In addition to the basic tools a number of other tools and pieces of equipment may be required as and when new work is undertaken. Some useful initial items are pliers, tweezers, hand vices, pin vices for holding small work or clamping pieces together. Three or four small G-clamps are also useful for holding pieces together when cutting, filing or soldering. For use in bending sheet pewter, some lengths of mild steel strip, say 30 cm (12 in.) long and 25 mm (1 in.) × 6 mm ($\frac{1}{4}$ in.) in section are useful and similarly some lengths of square section hardwood.

Care of tools

When first setting up the workshop do not initially buy more than the necessary basic tools. Only good-quality tools should be bought as these will wear out less quickly and work better than cheap tools. As work progresses and experience is gained, more tools will be required, but by this stage it will be much more obvious exactly what tools are needed.

Tools should be kept clean and free from rust and lightly oiled as and when required. Particular care must be taken with planishing hammers and stakes to see that the surfaces are kept in good condition. Scribers, centre punches and cutting snips should always be kept sharp. Hacksaw blades should be changed as soon as they become blunt. Do not cut wire with tin snips, as this damages the blades, use wire cutters or side cutters. Always keep drills sharp, and ground to the correct angle. Use the file brush regularly to keep the files free of clogging swarf, particularly solder.

When not in use, keep tools and equipment in drawers, boxes or racks. For workshops that are only used occasionally and left unheated, it is better to keep tools in drawers and boxes rather than in open racks, as they are less likely to be affected by rust caused by condensation.

Mallets

Mallets are made from boxwood, rawhide, rubber or plastic and are available in a range of weights and sizes. For use on pewter the softer mallets are to be preferred. A soft-faced hammer set is a good initial investment as this comes in a range of weights with four screw-in rubber-like heads, flat, dome, cone and wedge-shaped. Other shapes and sizes of mallets can be added as work progresses. A set that will cover most of the work likely to be encountered in the pewter workshop is as follows.

400 g (14 oz) soft-faced hammer set with four heads
600 g (21 oz) plastic mallet with screw-in flat heads
400 g (14 oz) rubber mallet
250 g (9 oz) pear-shaped hardwood mallet

When using mallets, take care that filings or pieces of metal do not become embedded in the faces as this could cause serious damage to the workpiece.

V Soldering

INTRODUCTION

Soldering is one of the most important techniques in the pewter workshop as it is the standard method of joining individual components to form an assembly. When carried out with skill and the correct materials, the joints are extremely difficult to detect.

SOLDER

The solders used in the pewter industry are classified as soft solders and are in the main tin–lead alloys, though pure tin and pewter itself is used in a number of cases depending upon a particular requirement.

Tin-based solders are produced in a number of grades to national standards, though a number of pewtersmiths do in fact make up solders to their own particular formulae. Three commonly used solders are (a) 63% tin, 37% lead; (b) 60% tin, 40% lead; and (c) 70% tin, 30% lead. These all have the same solidus temperature of 183°C (361°F), but their liquidus temperatures are respectively 183°C (361°F), 190°C (372°F) and 192°C (378°F). Note that the 63/37 solder has the same temperature for both solidus and liquidus and is therefore a eutectic. The others have a short pasty stage.

The standard solders are produced to exacting specifications usually by the companies which produce the basic pewter alloys. This consistency of performance is of extreme importance to the pewtersmith as the melting points are so close to that of the pewter itself that one must be sure that the solder will melt when expected. The solder alloys are prepared in a manner similar to other alloys, that is melted and mixed in iron melting pots. The molten solder is then cast into moulds to form sticks or bars, or poured direct into a machine with a rotating drum which is water-cooled and produces a continuous strip. A considerable volume of solder is produced in wire form by extrusion and wire drawing machines. The wire solder is produced in a range of diameters, wound on a reel, and is usually sold by weight. The wire form is best suited to the pewter workshop and is supplied on small reels and in one or two diameters. A suitable diameter for use in the pewter workshop is 1.5 mm (0.060 in.). Solder wire is also produced in an extruded form containing an inner core of flux so that no separate fluxing operation is necessary. The majority of flux-cored solders available are not suitable for pewter as the flux is too corrosive. Unless a cored solder is specifically recommended for use on pewter, its use should be avoided. Solder pastes and creams, which are mixtures of powdered solder and flux, are available in various grades. For certain assemblies of pewter these can be useful, but it is important to select the correct grade. The pastes tend to contain active fluxes, whilst the creams contain non-corrosive resin fluxes which are preferable for pewter.

FLUXES

The solder makes a joint by forming an amalgam with the mating surfaces. In order to do this, it must wet the corresponding surfaces. This wetting can only take place if the surfaces, and in fact the solders, are clean and free from oxides. The cleaning is carried out by a flux which is basically a weak acid mixture. Fluxes vary in nature depending upon the particular metals to be soldered. Some fluxes are very corrosive and it is important to use a flux specifically formulated for pewter. Commercial fluxes are available such as Fry's Oleic No. 9 or 10, Fry's Opal 575 or similar. One of the most common fluxes for use on pewter is a mixture of 9 parts glycerine and 1 part hydrochloric acid. This gives excellent results and little danger of corrosion or marking. A flux that is less liquid and perhaps more suitable for certain jobs is a resin and alcohol mixture to the desired consistency, a typical mixture being 25% resin, 75% alcohol. General tinning fluxes and some electrical fluxes should be avoided as they are usually fairly corrosive or otherwise unsuitable.

TECHNIQUE

The most convenient and widely used method of heating for soldering in the pewter industry is the gas/air torch or an LP gas torch. Soldering irons are rarely used as it is extremely difficult to control the heat input in a situation where the pewter melts only a few degrees above the solder itself. It is in fact the control of the heat that is the basis of the skill in soldering pewter. It is often said that pewter is easy to solder, whereas what is meant is that pewter solders easily because the amalgam between the solder and the pewter takes place so readily. The actual process of soldering is not so easy because of the small difference in the melting points of the solder and the pewter. This demands considerable skill in applying sufficient heat to melt the solder without melting the pewter. For this reason a very fine flame is used on the torch commonly called a needle flame. Most torches are capable of being fitted with a number of nozzles or burners and for use on pewter the finest nozzle or burner should be used. It is also important that the flame should be seen, so that only the end of the flame is in contact with the solder and the joint. If the soldering area is too brightly illuminated, it is not possible to see the flame. Lighting should be positioned with care and it is common practice for the pewtersmith to carry out the soldering operation in his own shadow, that is with his back to the main light source. The flame can then be seen quite clearly and the correct position maintained. This is of particular importance in soldering joints where there is the possibility of the flame being deflected, say from a handle or a curvature of a base. If the flame is moved too close in, there is the possibility of the flame being deflected to cover a relatively large area rather than the specific joint, with the consequent danger of burning or melting.

There are two basic methods of using the gas torch, either in a fixed position on the bench or held in the hand. If the torch is fixed then both hands are free to hold the work and apply the solder. In the case of the portable torch, the work must be supported in some way as both the hands are occupied; one holding the torch, the other the solder. Many pewtersmiths have two torches ready for use, one mounted on an adjustable clamp fixed to the bench, and one portable. During constant work, the torch remains lit, but it is important to reduce the flame to a luminous state so that it can be seen and is clear of any inflammable material. This is normally only possible with a gas/air torch and if a gas-only torch is used, it is preferable to turn off completely and relight when required.

Dependent upon the work in hand, the pewtersmith will use either the fixed or portable torch. Some use the fixed torch for all of the work, and others for part of the work and then change to the portable torch. Another, very useful, piece of equipment is a simple turntable, which is basically a horizontal plate mounted on a vertical spindle in some form of bearing so that the plate can rotate. The work is mounted on the plate and can then be rotated to the correct position for soldering.

There are two basic methods of applying the solder, either continuously from the solder wire or stick, or in the form of small pellets. The most common method in the pewter industry is to apply the solder continuously, usually direct from the reel. This method is to be preferred, though considerable skill and practice is required, as it gives a cleaner flowing joint with little or no surplus solder. It does however mean complete co-ordination of movement of the torch and the solder. The pellet method is simpler for the less skilled and the occasional job. With the latter method the work is supported on the bench or preferably the turntable and small pellets of solder are placed along the joint, ready for the application of the torch.

Soldering a side seam

The solder used is one of a high-tin content, such as a 70/30 or higher. It is essential that the edges are perfectly straight to make a close joint.

A fixed torch is used so that the pewtersmith can squeeze the joint together with his hand. If a portable torch was used the joint would have to be held together with wire or some form of wedging in a fixture. Either a length of solder wire is used or it can be drawn continuously from the reel. The end of the solder is dipped in flux, usually a glycerine flux, and wiped down the joint. Only a small amount of flux is required as the solder follows the flux, and surplus flux running over the sides can cause the solder to spread over the joint. In addition, the flux can stain the surface, and also, glycer-

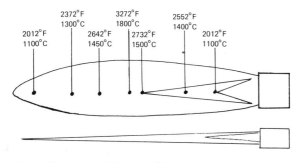

Diag. V:1   *Typical flame profiles.*

2372°F
1300°C

3272°F
1800°C

2552°F
1400°C

2012°F
1100°C

2642°F
1450°C

2732°F
1500°C

2012°F
1100°C

Fig. V:1 *Soldering the seam of a tankard using a fixed torch, PMC Ltd. Sheffield.*

Fig. V:2 *Soldering feet on to a vessel using a fixed torch, PMC Ltd. Sheffield.*

ine burns with an almost invisible flame. An excess could therefore carry a flame to the operator's hand.

The joint is brought into contact with the flame and passed to and fro to warm it up. A spot of solder is melted on to each end of the joint to hold it together. The joint is then passed under the flame with the solder wire touching as and when required so that the solder flows along the seam.

Soldering feet

Two methods are shown, using a fixed torch and a portable torch.

Using the fixed torch method the positions of the feet are first marked on the base with a pencil from a jig or a template. The pewtersmith holds the foot in position with his index finger and warms the joint by approaching the fixed flame. A glycerine flux could be used here, but the shape of the vessel is such that it could run in all directions. The more viscous resin flux is preferable in this instance. A spot of solder, a 60/40, is melted to tack the foot in position. The other two feet are tacked in a similar manner and all three checked for position. By manipulating the vessel around the flame and applying the solder at one or two points, the molten solder is flowed around the foot.

The alternative method is to use a portable torch and a turntable. The particular turntable top has been designed for the job, the vessel sitting on a

boss. The feet are pushed into position and initially tacked with a spot of solder. A glycerine flux could be used here with advantage as, by being applied to the top, it would flow down and around the joint. Further solder is applied and the flame moved around the joint so that the solder flows in.

Soldering a handle

The body of a tankard is supported on a soft cloth or sandbag so that it is firm. The handle is rested in position so that it is supported by the rim and if necessary can be held in place with soft iron bending wire. Flux is applied by dipping the stick of a solder in the flux pot and touching the joint. A portable torch is used and in this particular case, as the tankard is a heavy cast vessel, a little time is spent warming up the local area. A 60/40 solder tack is made in both positions to hold the handle firmly. By manipulating the torch and the solder stick, molten solder flows in around the joint.

Soldering a body

This is a good example of the use of a turntable, in the soldering together of the top and bottom of a cast vessel. The bottom is placed on the turntable and its top edge given a film of glycerine flux using a brush. The lower edge of the top section is fluxed in similar manner and the top section positioned on the bottom. Using a portable torch the joint is tacked in three places. Holding the flame in position, the turntable is rotated to warm up the joint area. With the flame held in an almost constant position, some solder is melted into the joint and the turntable moved around a few degrees. When there is sufficient solder around the joint, the solder stick is removed and the turntable rotated continuously

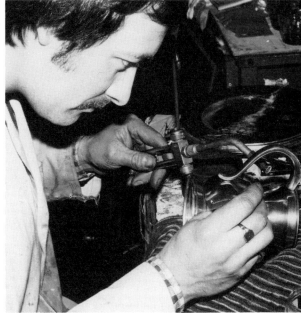

with the flame playing on the joint, flowing in the solder. If this is a drinking vessel, a high-tin solder would be used.

Soldering a baseplate

Two techniques are shown using the flowed solder method and the solder pellet method.

The flowed solder method uses a fixed torch with the pewtersmith initially holding the base plate and the body together with the left hand. The right hand holds the solder wire and the end of the wire is used to run a film of glycerine flux around the joint. A solder tack is made at each side to hold the base in position. The joint is then passed under the flame with the solder being applied, as and when required, until a smooth fillet of solder flows around the joint. A 60/40 solder would probably be used here as it melts at a lower temperature than the higher tin solder used for the vertical seam. Even then, care must be taken when passing the vertical seam with the torch to avoid melting out the original joint. In this situation it is possible to reduce this risk by painting the vertical seam with yellow ochre which acts as a heat barrier for the short time involved.

For the pellet method a turntable is used and the body positioned on the base plate and held there by a weight. Small pellets of solder 3 mm ($\frac{1}{8}$ in.) long are cut from solder wire and dropped into a tray containing some glycerine flux. A film of flux is also painted around the joint using a small brush. The pellets are picked up from the tray, using the end of

Fig. V:3   *Soldering feet on to a vessel using a portable torch and a turntable, PMC Ltd. Sheffield.*

Fig. V:4   *Soldering a handle to a tankard using a portable torch, A. E. Williams.*

the brush or tweezers, and placed against the joint, being spaced 6 mm ($\frac{1}{4}$ in.) apart. A portable torch is used and, by manipulating both the torch and the turntable, the joint is warmed up. Starting at one end, the flame is held until the first pellet melts and begins to flow. This occurs just after the glycerine flux begins to boil, which is a useful guide. Once the solder begins to flow the torch is moved steadily along the joint with the molten solder following behind it.

It is with this sort of joint in the right-angled corner of a box that extra care must be taken with the flame. If moved in too close, the flame will be deflected up the sides of the box with the danger of burning or melting. The torch should be held so that the fine point of the flame plays well into the corner.

Soldering bases to tankards

For this operation a turntable is again of considerable assistance. The bases are relatively heavy compared with the side walls of the tankard and therefore some preheating is desirable. In a high-production workshop it is common practice to mount half a dozen or more bases on the turntable and preheat them, whilst rotating the table. The

tankard body is then positioned on the uppermost base. The solder wire is dipped in a glycerine flux and wiped around the joint as the turntable revolves. The torch flame is then played upon the joint and the solder wire touched and melted as required. The turntable is kept revolving at a speed to match the smooth flow of solder into the joint.

The procedure is repeated with the next tankard body, and so on.

Other methods

For small fine work such as attachments of cast military models or jewellery, a torch is not always convenient. In these cases it is possible to use an electric soldering iron fitted with a very fine suitably shaped bit. Alternatively, a spot-welding technique may be used. For this, the pewter piece is connected

Fig. V:5 *Soldering the top to the bottom of a cast vessel using a portable torch and a turntable, James Smellie Ltd.*

Fig. V:6 *Soldering the base to a flask using a fixed torch, Tether Manufacturing Ltd.*

Fig. V:7 *Soldering the base to a cylinder using pellets of solder, J. A. Murrell.*

Fig. V:8 *Soldering the base to the body of a tankard, PMC Ltd. Sheffield.*

to one pole of a battery and a small soldering bit is connected to the other pole. Resistance heating takes place and the contact surfaces are melted and bond together as they solidify.

SUMMARY

Once the technique is mastered, there is considerable satisfaction in producing a well-soldered joint that is extremely difficult to detect. The art is to be in control of the flame, not to use too much solder, and just sufficient flux to clean the joint. Gaps should be minimal and it is better to spend a few minutes with a file to make close fitting joints rather than attempt to fill gaps with solder. The apprentice and the novice are well advised to practice on old scraps of pewter before attempting to solder a complete piece of work. These practice runs will give experience in size of flame, feel of the torch, action of the flux and an insight into knowing when the solder is about to melt. Once the confidence or feel has been gained, the technique can be further developed by the craftsman to suit one's own individuality.

VI Hand-Forming Techniques

INTRODUCTION

Prior to the introduction of forming pewter by spinning on a lathe, the only alternative to casting was to form by hand. Plates, chargers and trays were beaten out by hand by 'sadware men' and pots and vessels were formed and beaten by 'holloware men'. Although some handwork is still required on certain products, that is apart from soldering, little hand-forming is carried out on a commercial basis, mainly because of the time and labour cost involved. It is important, however, that the future craftsman and apprentice be trained in all of the hand-forming techniques, in order to understand the material and the total craft. For the individual craftsman and the special piece of work the techniques are part of the daily life.

The basic techniques are common to all workers of sheet metal, whether they be tinsmiths, coppersmiths, silversmiths or pewtersmiths, as are the basic tools. The processes can be classified under four main headings, hollowing, raising, folding and seaming, and any one particular piece of work may use one or all of the processes. All of the hand-forming techniques are used in the production of the articles described in the following text.

ROUND BOWL AND PORRINGER

Hollowing

A round bowl can be formed by hollowing, raising, or by a combination of both techniques. Basically, hollowing is used for shallow work, and raising for deep work. The process of hollowing tends to stretch metal, whilst raising tends to compress it. It follows therefore that if a bowl is to be formed up from a flat disc, then both processes are liable to be used. The round bowl, whilst being a piece of work in itself, is often an integral part of a more complex piece, the basic forming processes being common. Having decided upon the finished dimensions of the bowl, a flat circular disc is cut to a diameter determined by the method outlined in the section on working drawings (pp. 35–6). The thickness of the pewter sheet is to some extent dependent upon the final use of the article, but as some thinning is liable to take place it should not be too thin. An approximate guide is as follows:

125 mm (5 in.) dia. bowl 1.25 mm (0.05 in.) thick
230 mm (9 in.) dia.   1.50 mm (0.06 in.) thick
300 mm (12 in.) dia.   1.75 mm (0.07 in.) thick

Having cut the disc to shape, the sharp edges should be eased with a smooth file. If the bowl is to be free standing, or a porringer, then the central part needs to remain flat and a circle should be drawn in pencil to a suitable diameter. As a further aid for the inexperienced a series of circles 12 mm ($\frac{1}{2}$ in.) apart can be drawn in pencil, on the disc, as a guide when forming.

The bowl can be hollowed on a sandbag, but the preferred method is to use a series of hollowed blocks of wood. The first block is shallow and known as a starting block, the others as hollowing blocks. It is possible to use a block hollowed to the exact shape and beat the bowl into this mould. This method limits the size of the bowl and it is better to use two or three hollowing blocks and finish the bowl on a stake, which gives much more flexibility.

The bowl is started by raising the edge in the starting block. A mallet of boxwood or hide, preferably with a rounded head, is used, a tinman's bossing mallet is ideal, and overlapping blows are struck about 18 mm ($\frac{3}{4}$ in.) in from the edge. The disc is held at a slight angle and the blows are kept at an even pressure all round the disc. The blows must overlap or else dents and crinkling are liable to occur. A rhythm should be kept up, of three blows and then move the disc for the next three blows and so on. Work continues in this manner, gradually moving in towards the centre. As the bowl deepens, a deeper hollowing block is used to suit the curvature. If the bowl is to be mounted on a foot, the beating continues to the centre. If the base is to

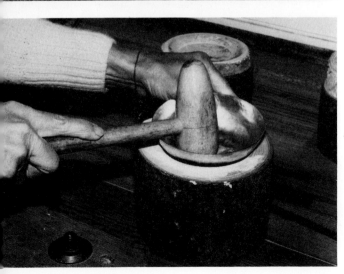

Fig. VI:1 *Raising the edge in a hollowing block, J. A. Murrell. (top left)*

Fig. VI:2 *First stages of hollowing to produce a bowl, J. A. Murrell. (middle left)*

Fig. VI:3 *Completing the hollowing process in a deeper block, J. A. Murrell. (bottom left)*

Fig. VI:4 *Setting the base with a setting block, J. A. Murrell. (top right)*

Fig. VI:5 *Planishing the bowl on a stake, J. A. Murrell. (middle right)*

remain flat, then the beating stops at the drawn circle.

As soon as the shape is formed, the bowl can be finished on a stake. The stake can be of metal or wood and a half-moon stake or round-head stake can be used. The bowl is held on the stake and working from the centre outwards, it is smoothed off using a mallet with a flat head, preferably hide or rubber. Blows again overlap and the bowl is rotated continuously. By working from the centre outwards, the sides will be steepened or raised to suit the desired shape.

If the bowl is to be free standing, the next stage is to set the bottom. This is done by using a circular piece of wood, placing the bowl on a flat surface and hammering the setting block in with a mallet. A block of the exact size can be used or alternatively a smaller diameter setter can be slowly moved around to cover the required area.

The edge of the bowl will be uneven because of the forming process, so the bowl is stood on its base and the edge marked out, using a scribing block or surface gauge. The edge is then trimmed to the line using a smooth file. At this stage the bowl may be regarded as finished with regard to forming, and ready for planishing if required.

Planishing

Planishing must not be confused with decorative hammered finishing. The metal is smoothed off by hammering with a special polished hammer on a polished metal stake. Unlike raising, where the hammer blow is struck beyond the contact point of the metal and the stake, in order to move the metal, planishing squeezes the metal between the hammer and the stake. It is important, therefore, that the stake is of a suitable shape to suit the curvature of the bowl. Planishing hammers commonly have one square face and one round face, each face being only slightly domed. The round end should be used on a bowl and the hammer blows should be light and overlap each other. The object of planishing is to even out the surface stresses in the metal, to smooth it and to stiffen it. It is absolutely essential to ensure that both hammer and stake are clean, polished and free from swarf or filings, lest these be hammered into the surface.

Finishing

If only a plain bowl is required, all that remains is to polish it, which should be carried out as explained in the section on finishing (pp. 134–8).

Fig. VI:6 *Hand-formed porringer with cast handles, J. A. Murrell.*

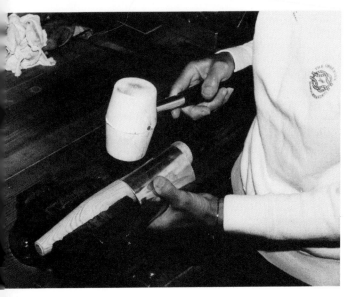

CYLINDRICAL TOBACCO JAR

This is an exercise in cylindrical development and is drawn out as described in the section on working drawings (pp. 35–6), once the diameter and height have been determined. In order to ensure a perfect fit and match, the lid and the body are made from the same cylinder, so the depth of the lid must be added to the height, in the development.

Rolling and seaming

The developed sheet is cut to shape and all the burrs removed from the edges with a small file. The two end edges of the sheet must be perfectly straight and square, for these butt together to form the seam.

A cylinder stake or length of steel shaft is held in the vice and the cylinder is formed by hand around the stake. Pewter is soft so it is possible to smooth the cylinder with a stroking motion of the hand, pressure being applied at the base of the thumb. A rubber or wooden mallet with a flat face is used to gently beat down the two edges straight and smooth. The cylinder is then squeezed to make the edges overlap and then opened and allowed to close, so that there is some springy tension butting the edges together.

Soft iron binding wire is used to clamp the edges together, and the seam is soldered by one of the techniques described in the section on soldering (pp. 48–52). After soldering, the seam is hammered down using a flat-faced hammer on the cylindrical stake.

The cylinder is then formed into a perfectly circular shape on a wooden or metal stake using a soft-

Fig. VI:7 *Forming the cylinder using a rubber mallet and wooden former, J. A. Murrell.*

Fig. VI:8 *The completed jar and lid, J. A. Murrell.*

faced mallet for smoothing. An initial planishing process can also take place at this stage, using the square face of the planishing hammer and a polished metal stake.

Bottom and top

Two discs are cut some 12 mm ($\frac{1}{2}$ in.) larger in diameter than the cylinder. The top and bottom edges of the cylinder are checked for level and squareness and trimmed if required. The ends should be finally squared off by holding the cylinder square and upright and rubbing it across a sheet of fine emery cloth on a perfectly flat surface. The discs are then soldered to each end of the cylinder using pellets of solder or the flow method. A turntable is a distinct advantage during this soldering operation. Using curved snips the excess metal is trimmed from the top and bottom discs and the edges filed flush. The cylinder is quite rigid at this stage and an initial polishing operation can be carried out all over, including the top and the bottom.

Lid

The lid is formed by cutting it from the sealed cylinder. Using a scribing block or surface gauge, a line is scribed around the cylinder at the desired depth. The cylinder is then held on a sandbag, or a pile of soft cloth, and using a junior hacksaw with a very fine blade, the cylinder is sawn through. Great care should be taken not to let the saw slip and mark the cylinder. Once separated, the edges of the lid and the body are smoothed off by rubbing on the flat sheet of emery cloth.

The next stage is to fit a band over which the lid will sit to form a tight seal. A strip of pewter 18 mm ($\frac{3}{4}$ in.) wide is cut and rolled to form a ring that is a push fit inside the cylinder. The two ends of the ring are soldered together to form a butt joint which is then cleaned off to produce a smooth ring. The ring, or band, is then pushed inside the cylinder to half its depth. The band should be held in position by three or four clips to prevent it moving during soldering. Hair grips make suitable clips and should be used with thin asbestos strips between the grip and the pewter. The band is then soldered into position. A lower melting point solder than was used elsewhere should be used for this, to avoid opening up the main seam. Surplus solder should be filed off so that there is a sharp right angle between the edge of the cylinder and the band. A needle file is the ideal tool for this. The lid can now be fitted into position.

A knob or handle can be designed to fit on to the lid.

BUD VASE

The design of this small vase is an exercise in development, folding and seaming.

Development

The basic form is a square pyramid and the construction of the development is as described in the section on working drawings (pp. 32–6).

Once the development has been laid out on the sheet of pewter, it can be cut out with tin snips. It is important to cut on the lines, straight and true in order to produce good butt joints. The three major fold lines and the four minor ones should be scored with the end of a bent scriber, or a scoring tool, as this makes for easier folding.

Folding and seaming

A pair of folding bars are required for this operation in order to ensure straight folds. The bars are basically two straight strips of metal or hardwood with the sharp edge just removed. One bar must be of a depth less than the dimension of the top edge of the vase as the sheet has to fold around one bar. The bars can be bolted together at one end with a nut and bolt, or a G-clamp can be used.

Using a vice, the whole assembly is clamped together in correct alignment. Great care should be taken in this alignment, for once the fold is made, it is impossible to alter it. The fold is best made by using a strip of wood to push the sheet over in one operation and then smooth it down. Once the body

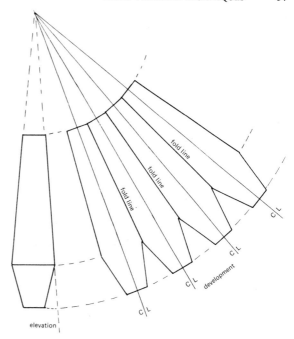

Diag. VI:1 *Layout and development of bud vase.*

has been formed square, it should be squeezed gently so that the butt joint is tight. Some working and smoothing on the folding bars may be necessary to ensure a close fit of the joint.

Whilst it is possible to make all of the folds and then solder all the joints at one time, this is not recommended. It is preferable to solder the main seam first which gives an opportunity for the body to be re-squared and makes the folding in of the bottom four pieces much easier.

To solder the main joint the body can be wired as the cylinder was, or it can be wedged between two firebricks, or pieces of wood, to keep the joint closed. A high melting point solder should be used for this joint and the soldering technique should be as described in the section on soldering (pp. 48–52).

The soldered joint should then be cleaned up and filed smooth and the body put back on the folding bars and re-squared if required.

There is a little difficulty in folding in the bottom four sides as the folding former used inside the vase has to be narrower than the top opening in order to get it in. Provided the fold lines were well scored and a piece of flat wood larger than the side piece is used, the side will fold along the line. A little squeezing and smoothing, with a block of wood, may be required to ensure that the four joints close tightly. The four joints are then soldered as before, though this time a lower melting point can

Fig. VI:9 *Folding the body of the vase using folding bars and block of wood, J. A. Murrell. (top left)*

Fig. VI:10 *Ready for soldering the base. Note the weight to hold the assembly together, J. A. Murrell. (top right)*

Fig. VI:11 *The completed bud vase, J. A. Murrell. (left)*

be used to reduce the risk of opening up the main joint. The joints can be filed smooth with a fine file and the whole body polished with a very fine emery cloth or a flexible silicone carbide block to a satin finish.

Base

In order to give some bottom weight, the baseplate is a simple casting, or alternatively, it could be built up from a number of thick sheets of pewter soldered together. After casting, the base is filed to shape and a square section filed in so that the body fits tightly over it for alignment when soldering.

When soldering the base, it is an advantage to place a weight on top of the vase and use a turntable.

The final operation on the vase is to bell out the top edges slightly. This can be done on the edge of the bench or a piece of hardwood held in the vice using a light hammer. The edges can then be smoothed off by rubbing with a piece of wood, cut to a close fit inside the top. A final polish completes the piece of work.

HIP FLASKS

Hip flasks are produced either from flat sheet or from pressings.

Flat sheet method

The developed sheet is simply a rectangle, of a precise length and height, with its edges cut perfectly straight. A curved wooden or steel former is used and the pewter sheet is folded around it so that the butt joint runs down one side rather than down a face. Folding takes place on a flat surface using the hands to smooth the metal around the shape.

The body is squeezed to make the joint tight and the seam soldered. In this case a high-tin content solder is used, as a flask is a drinking vessel.

The top and bottom are pieces of rectangular plate cut so that there is an overlap of approximately 6 mm ($\frac{1}{4}$ in.) all round. The top plate has a hole drilled in the centre prior to soldering, so that there is no danger of air pressure building up or swarf being left inside the flask. After soldering, the excess metal is trimmed off, using curved snips, and the joint filed smooth.

The neck and the cap require the use of a lathe, preferably with some form of screw cutting, though hand thread chasing can be used. Two small pewter castings are required so that the pieces can be turned. The diameter must, of course, suit the thickness of the flask. As pewter is soft the thread should not be too fine, 16 tpi or 1.5 mm pitch is suitable. A piece of cork is also required to fit inside the cap to form a liquid seal. The neck is soldered to suit the top plate which completes the assembly of the flask.

When polishing the flask on a polishing machine, the flask should be filled with cold water. It has been found that the unequal distribution of heat generated by polishing can cause severe distortion which cannot be recovered, thus ruining the flask.

Pressings

An alternative method of producing flasks is to use two pressings. These are produced from a die and a mould, in a press. The pressings come out of the die with a flange all the way round, which has to be trimmed off. The two halves are then seam soldered together. A separate base plate is stamped out and this is then soldered to the body. Touch marks and any other information must of course be stamped in prior to soldering.

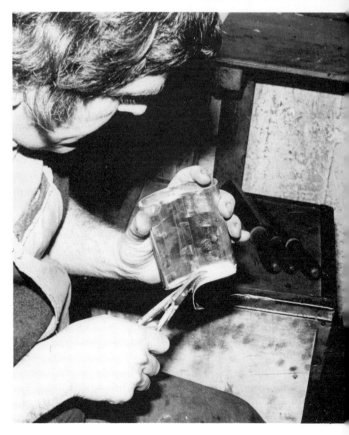

Fig. VI:12 *Forming the body of a hip flask, Tether Manufacturing Ltd.*

Fig. VI:13 *Cutting away the surplus metal using curved tin snips, Tether Manufacturing Ltd.*

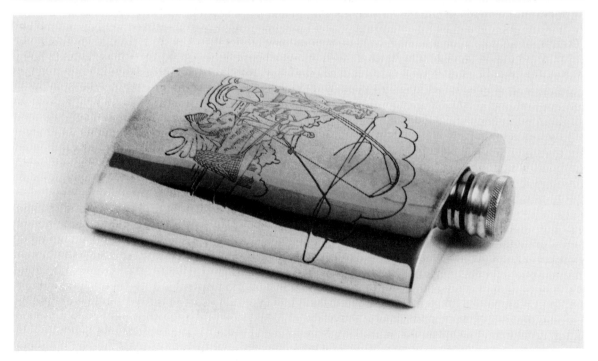

CIRCULAR FLASKS

Circular flasks are produced in a similar manner, though the two halves are usually spinnings rather than pressings.

Fig. VI:14   *The two major pressings and other parts for a hip flask, James Dixon & Sons Ltd.*

Fig. VI:15   *A completed hip flask, Tether Manufacturing Ltd.*

BOXES

Boxes give considerable scope to the designer/craftsman's imagination with regard to size, dimension, type of lid, decoration and finish. There are three basic hand methods of forming a box from a flat sheet of pewter (a) form the sides from one strip and solder on to a base plate; (b) develop the complete box and fold up the four sides, soldering each corner; (c) develop the base and two sides and fold up and then solder on separate ends. For a simple box, the latter method is to be preferred as it is economical in material and only two accurate folds are required.

Development

The development is a simple rectangle, of length equal to the box and width, equal to the width of the box plus twice the depth.

Folding

The rectangle should be carefully cut with snips and the edges checked for straightness and squareness. The two fold lines should be scored to about half the thickness of the material if a sharp-edged box is required. If a radiused edge box is required then the fold lines should not be scored. Using the folding bars and a block of wood the sides are folded and smoothed over perfectly square.

Ends

Two end plates are cut, approximately 6 mm ($\frac{1}{4}$ in.) larger on three sides to form a shelf for the solder. The folded body is stood on the end plate, so that one edge is flush with the top of the box leaving the protruding areas for soldering. A weight should be placed on the top, to hold the body down on the end plate. The end plate can now be soldered into position, the use of a turntable aiding this operation. Surplus metal is cut away with snips and the edges filed flush and smooth. Masking tape applied to the box adjacent to the edge reduces the risk of file marks on the main body. The other end plate is fitted in a similar manner.

Lids

Lids can be of three types, external fitting, internal fitting or flush fitting, depending upon the design.

External fitting

The development of the lid is similar to that of the box, except that the width of the rectangle should be cut a few millimetres wider than the total theoretical width, and the length must be equal to the finished box. Only one fold line should be drawn initially, to the depth required. This is then folded up square in the folding bars. The box is then placed on the partially formed lid, tight up against the folded side. The opposite fold line can now be scribed off on the lid using the side of the box to determine the

dimension. The second side of the lid can now be folded, but the scribed line should be just inside the folding bars so that the fold is beyond the line and not on it. Having made the fold, check that the lid fits as required. If too loose or too tight the folds can be corrected slightly by cutting a piece of wood to the exact size of the box and with the aid of a mallet stretching or compressing to suit. If the error was too great such as folding the wrong side of the line, it is better to scrap the piece and start again. Once the lid is fitting correctly the second side, which is deeper, should be marked out and cut to match the first side.

The ends of the lid are made and fitted in a similar manner to those of the box. A jeweller's peg fitted to the bench is a considerable aid in filing the edges of the box and the lid.

Flush fitting

For a flush-fitting lid, the lid must be exactly the same dimensions as the box. To simplify this, it is an advantage to fold the box over a wooden former of exact size rather than use the folding bars. The lid can be folded over the same former thus ensuring an exact match.

In order for the lid to fit, a band must be fitted inside the box over which sits the lid. A strip of pewter is cut and formed into a rectangle to fit tightly inside the box. This is inserted, to half its depth, and soldered into position. The band should be held with clips so that it does not move during soldering. The technique is as described in the construction of the cylindrical tobacco jar (see pp. 56–7).

Before fitting the band into the box, the internal finish of the box should be applied, whether this be polished or textured, as it may be difficult to do this with the band in position.

Internal fitting

For an internal-fitting lid with an overlapping top, a band is again required. In this case, however, the band is soldered to the underside of the lid and is a slide fit in the box.

Decoration and finish

Boxes can be highly polished or satin finished using the methods outlined in the section on finishing (see pp. 134–8). They are, however, often difficult to polish inside and consideration should be given to a textured finish applied with small wire brushes or stones. The effect of a polished outside and a textured inside can be very pleasing.

Decoration can be engraving, etching or appliqué, especially on the lids.

Fig. VI:16   *Showing the parts for a box: folded body and lid, separate end plates, strip for the band, J. A. Murrell. (top left)*

Fig. VI:17   *The cast appliqué and the lid drilled ready for fitting, J. A. Murrell. (left)*

Fig. VI:18   *The completed box with external fitting lid, J. A. Murrell. (top right)*

Fig. VI:19   *A selection of small boxes, Tether Manufacturing Ltd. (opposite)*

Appliqué

Appliqué design can be built up by using separate pieces of pewter sheet soldered together, or different materials can be used. In the examples illustrated, cast plaques were used.

The plaque or appliqué design can be soldered to the lid by soldering all round the edge. Considerable skill in soldering is required to do this and though it is well within the capabilities of the skilled pewter-mith it can prove difficult for the less skilled. A simpler method is to tack it in from the underside of the lid. Four holes are drilled in the lid, within the dimensions of the plaque. The plaque or appliqué is positioned on the lid in the desired position and held there by masking tape or pieces of plasticine. The lid is then reversed onto the soldering bench and four spots of solder are applied through the holes, filling them up if so desired. This method attaches the appliqué firmly to the lid without the danger of solder running across the finished surface of the lid.

SMALL BOXES

Snuff boxes and pill boxes can be made as outlined above, or can be produced by a variety of methods.

As they are small, they can be made from simple shallow pressings produced on a hand-operated fly press. They can be made from spinnings, which can be produced on a relatively small simple lathe. Alternatively, they can be cast in rubber or plaster moulds.

Lids can be cut from thick sheet in one piece, or built up from thin sheet or, alternatively, cast,

similar to the plaque described in appliqué design (p. 62). There is, therefore, considerable scope for the designer/craftsman using relatively simple equipment and small quantities of material.

Hinges

Hinged lids are very common on the smaller boxes and can of course be fitted to larger boxes. Hinges are also used on lidded articles such as teapots, coffee pots, tankards and flagons.

There are two methods of making hinges, either from tubing and sheet, or by casting. Most hinges used for pewter are bearer plate hinges, that is the tubular rotating sections are part of or attached to small plates. These plates or bearers are then soldered to the particular lid and body. In the silver industry it is common to use only the tubular sections of a hinge and solder these directly to a lid or body, unless of course the shape demands a bearer plate. With pewter, this method is usually not strong enough because of the softness and lack of stiffness of the material. For the same reason, hinges on pewter work are less delicate than those generally seen on silverware. These points must be borne in mind during the design stage of a hinged item. For strength and rigidity, a hinge should consist of at least five tubular sections, and it is common practice to fit these so that three are fixed and two are on the moving part.

Cast hinges

Hinges can be cast in metal, rubber or plaster moulds. Since the advent of centrifugal rubber mould casting, the majority are produced by this means, as quite a number can be cast in one operation.

They can of course be cast individually in simple rubber moulds. A pattern is required for each half of the hinge and the mould designed so that a false pin can be inserted in the mould and the hinge cast around it. This avoids any drilling operation and makes for good alignment.

For a few-off, or occasional use, it is possible to use a commercial hinge as a pattern. Small solid brass cabinet hinges have suitable proportions with regard to thickness and tube diameter.

Made-up hinge

In order to make up a hinge, some short lengths of tubing are required and some heavy gauge sheet. Pewter tubing is very difficult to obtain commercially, so it will have to be made up by rolling and soldering and then drawing it down to size through a wire drawing plate. This is a time-consuming process and it is probably better to use nickel silver tubing, which can be obtained through jewellery findings supplies. Nickel silver gives a reasonable colour match with pewter. Alternatively pewter rod can be cast in simple plaster moulds and turned and drilled on a small lathe to produce tubing.

The bearer plates are cut from heavy gauge sheet, say 1.7 mm (0.070 in.) to the size required. A slight bevel should be filed on one long edge of each piece. The two pieces with the bevels adjacent to each other should then be clamped in a vice. The bevels will form a small V-shaped groove which will act as a guide for a round file. Using a suitable

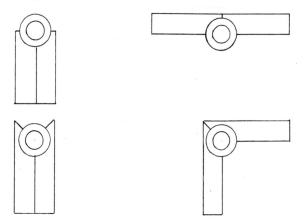

Diag. VI:2   *Showing hinge construction.*

diameter round file, a groove is filed to suit the tubing. If the hinge is to open right up, the groove should be filed until the tubing is in, to half its diameter. To stop the hinge opening no more than 90°, the groove should be filed to the complete diameter of the tube.

The tubing is cut into five equal lengths and soldered to the bearer plates, three to one plate and two to the other, using a pin to align them. A pin is fitted and the hinge is ready to be soldered to the piece of work as required. In order to seal the pin it can be cut a little short and the two open ends of the hinge tubes filled with a dab of solder.

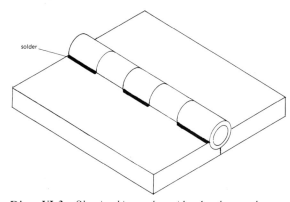

solder

Diag. VI:3   *Showing hinge tubes soldered to bearer plates.*

DEEP BOWLS

For deep bowls and articles such as goblets or pots, the hollowing technique is insufficient and these must be raised.

Raising

In raising most of the work is carried out on the outside surface of the disc of metal as opposed to hollowing, where most of the hammer work is on

the inside surface. Invariably some hollowing is carried out initially before raising.

A metal or wooden raising stake is required which has a curved or rounded surface. It is also possible to use a round-headed stake or a half-moon stake, as what is required is a stake with a surface curved in all directions. Pewter can be raised with a hammer or a mallet. A raising hammer has a relatively wide head of narrow rounded section, whilst a mallet has a wedge-shaped head with a rounded edge.

Having determined the diameter and thickness of the flat pewter disc it should be hollowed slightly on a sandbag or starting block exactly as described in the first stage of hollowing a bowl. The reason for this process, also known as blocking, is to give the disc some form prior to raising. It is extremely difficult to hold and start raising with a flat disc and there is a danger of buckling the sheet. The partially formed bowl is up-ended and a series of concentric circles about 6 mm ($\frac{1}{4}$ in.) apart drawn on the underside. These are used as a guide for the hammer.

Starting from the innermost circle the bowl is held on the stake tangential to the curve. Using the circular guidelines, blows are struck just above the point of contact, thus decreasing the diameter by compressing the metal. The three-rhythm technique should be used, that is, three overlapping blows and then move the bowl round slightly. Work continues progressively from circle to circle. The metal above the line of the blows will be seen to gradually buckle so every now and again these should be gently hammered out on the stake, using a flat-headed mallet. This should only be done if the buckling is severe, as there is a danger of stretching the metal. The raising process is continued up to the edge of the bowl. It is useful to use a template to confirm the shape, and this also indicates where further raising is required.

Once the shape is formed, the top edge can be marked out using a surface gauge and trimmed with snips and a file. The top edge can be thickened up by a process known as caulking, which is using the raising hammer directly down on the edge. The bowl can be supported on a sandbag or held in the

Fig. VI:20 *First stages in raising a bowl, J. A. Murrell.*

Fig. VI:21 *Further stages in raising a bowl, J. A. Murrell.*

Fig. VI:22 *The finished raised bowl with raising mallet and planishing hammer, J. A. Murrell.*

Fig. VI:23   *Hand-raised bowl with foot, J. A. Murrell. (left)*

Fig. VI:24   *The machined castings of rim and base ready for soldering to the body, J. A. Murrell. (opposite left)*

Fig. VI:25   *The completed jar and lid, J. A. Murrell. (opposite right)*

lap. After caulking the outside of the edge may need smoothing off again on the stake.

Further smoothing of the vessel can be done with a flat-faced mallet on a suitably shaped stake, or it can be planished with a planishing hammer as previously explained.

Further work and finish is as required by the design of the piece.

The use of the mallet or a hammer is ultimately one of personal choice, so the craftsman new to this work should practice with both. Normally, the blows are struck away from the body with the craftsman standing in front of the work. Some craftsmen find it more comfortable to set the stake lower and hammer towards the body. Again, both methods should be tried to determine the most comfortable method.

CONICAL JAR WITH LID

This particular piece has been designed to be produced in a small pewtershop as an exercise in a number of techniques.

Body

The body is a straightforward conical development rolled by hand. It is essential that the two edges are perfectly straight in order to form a good seam. The main seam is then soldered, either by using pellets of solder, or by flowing from the solder stick as described in the section on soldering (pp. 48–50). After soldering, the seam is hammered down on a steel stake and cleaned off with file and emery if required. Using a mallet and the steel stake, the conical body is smoothed and made perfectly circular.

Rim and base

The rim and base are simple castings, which are then machined on a small lathe. Alternatively, a base can be made by soldering together a number of sheets of heavy gauge pewter. The rim can be made by forming a ring from a strip of heavy gauge sheet.

The base is machined to a stepped shape, the top step being a tight fit into the bottom of the conical body. The rim is machined out so that it is a push fit on the outside of the top of the conical body.

The base and the ring are soldered to the body using the techniques previously explained. A turntable is a useful aid in soldering bases and rims.

The assembled body is then polished by hand or machine.

Lid

The lid is a simple spinning capable of being produced on a small lathe with a single spinning tool.

After spinning to shape the metal is trimmed back to the designed depth of the lid and one or two decorative grooves cut in. The lid can be polished prior to removal from the spinning chuck.

Motif

The lid can be left plain or can be fitted with a knob or appliqué design.

TRAYS

Trays are formed from flat sheet by sinking or beating down. Small trays can be completely beaten down into a shaped mould, turned or carved from

hardwood. Larger trays, or irregular shaped trays, are beaten down, on air, over the edge of a wooden stake. As the process stretches the material, the blank disc of pewter need only be to the finished dimension, plus an allowance for cleaning up. Sinking can be carried out on pewter with a ball pein hammer or a similar shaped mallet, such as the small end of a bossing or tinman's mallet.

Using a mould

If a wooden mould is used, the blank disc should be marked out with pencil compasses to a diameter to suit the mould. A second circle is drawn inside the first about 10 mm ($\frac{3}{8}$ in.) smaller in radius. These two concentric circles provide a guide for the hammer.

With the blank disc held firmly on the mould, overlapping hammer blows are struck all the way round between the concentric circles. This process is repeated two or three times which results in the tray having a circular groove in it. The rim should now be flattened with a planishing hammer to level it off. The centre of the tray is then beaten down, starting from the centre in a circular motion working out to the original groove. A planishing hammer or small mallet can be used for this, but care must be taken not to damage the curve of the original sinking. The sinking should be finally formed by holding the tray firmly in the mould and beating down with overlapping blows to a perfect fit. The sound of the blow is a good guide as to whether or not the particular area being struck is right down on to the surface of the mould. If the metal is already down in contact, the blow will sound dead as opposed to a slight ring if it is not.

Using a stake

Whilst the mould makes it easy to form a shape it is limited to the one size. A more flexible system of working is to use a wooden stake and beat down on air. The stake consists of a piece of hardwood held in a vice with the end grain uppermost. The stake can be wedge-shaped or filed or curved to a shape similar to the desired shape of the tray. A pencil circle or line is drawn on the pewter sheet to indicate the rim. The sheet is held with the rim flat on top of the stake and hammering is carried out just inside the pencil circle. Only one row of overlapping blows is used, which in effect beats down a groove just inside the rim line. Hammering continues until the required depth is reached. Normally trays are relatively shallow and three times around is probably sufficient.

The tray is then laid on a flat surface and beaten down with overlapping blows from the centre outwards. The rim can be flattened from the back using a piece of wood and a mallet. The sinking is completed by holding the tray at an angle on a hardwood edge and beating down into the recess. Further planishing of the bottom and rim is then required to level off and confirm the inside of the rim. After flattening and levelling, the outside edge of the rim can be trimmed and filed to shape.

The use of the stake allows for a variety of shapes and forms of trays to be produced without the expense and inconvenience of carving moulds.

OTHER HAND PROCESSES

Shrinking and belling out

With an article such as a vase or a cup it may be required to shrink in the bottom and bell out the top.

The main body can be a straightforward conical development, rolled by hand and seamed. The bottom end can be drawn in by a process known as shrinking. A steel, or wooden, stake with a rounded end is required for this. A mallet with a flat face of rubber or leather is preferable to a hammer because of its gentler action.

The conical body is slipped over the stake, with the end of the cone hanging over the rounded end of the stake. Using light blows, the end is gradually beaten over, starting off by moving the body an eighth of a turn to form a rough octagon. Then, the eight corners are beaten down and so on. By beating and rotating, the form will gradually take shape and a smooth surface will result. The process must be gradual, as even with a small shrinkage there is a lot of metal to compress and it is very easy to get a crease in the metal.

Belling out is carried out on a cylindrical stake of metal, or wood, or over the edge of a bench, or shaped piece of wood. The desired radius of the belled rim dictates the shape of the former. A round-headed mallet, such as a bossing mallet, is the preferred tool. A pencil line drawn around the inside of the conical body is a guide to keep the belling to an even depth. The mallet blows should overlap as the body is slowly turned. Work should start at the extreme edge and progress inwards as the bell mouth is formed. As pewter is soft, the shape can be smoothed off by rubbing round with a piece of shaped hardwood.

In both shrinking and belling, great care must be taken when working near the seam of a soldered body.

SIMPLE SPOUTS

Spouts can be formed directly from the main body of a vessel or be developed separately and soldered on. Complex spouts can be developed, but in the case of pewter are far easier produced by casting as explained in the section on slush casting (see pp. 98–100).

Fig. VI:26   *First stage in sinking a tray, J. A. Murrell.*

Fig. VI:27   *Flattening a sunk tray, J. A. Murrell.*

Fig. VI:28   *Shrinking in the bottom of a vase or cup, J. A. Murrell.*

Direct forming

For a directly formed spout allowance must be made in the original flat development. The conical development should be drawn in the normal manner and then the top profile modified to give sufficient metal to form the spout. At the same time the profile can also be modified to give a sweeping curved form to the top of the vessel.

The vessel is rolled and seamed, and then the spout is beaten out to a suitable form. Self-contained spouts are generally small, so a wooden former filed and carved to shape is easy to make. The spout is beaten into this form using a wedge-shaped mallet.

DEVELOPED SPOUT

The development for a simple spout is basically similar to that of half of a cone. With allowance for a lip the development can be called kite-shaped.

If no exact dimensions are available, say from a drawing or a model, it is preferable to make the developments in paper initially and try the paper spout against the vessel for shape and size. Having determined this, the metal spout can be cut out and folded to shape around a wooden former.

The spout is then filed to suit the profile of the vessel, and this must be a very good fit in order to ensure a good soldered joint. The spout is held in position on the vessel and the internal profile is scribed on to the wall of the vessel. The aperture is cut out, within the scribed outline leaving about $1\frac{1}{2}$ mm ($\frac{1}{16}$ in.) of land to be filed off after soldering. It is advisable to tack the spout into position and check the alignment prior to soldering. After soldering, the aperture is filed out to suit exactly the profile of the spout. A great number of variations of conical, or part conical, spouts are possible by developing and rolling up from flat sheet. Complex curved and shaped spouts can be developed from flat sheet, but in the case of pewter, which is easy to cast, it is preferable to make a wax model and use this to make a mould for slush casting the item.

HANDLES

Simple handles can be profiled and cut from heavy gauge sheet and then bent to shape. For more complex forms it is again easier to make up wax or plasticine models and make castings from them.

PROFILING

Jugs and vases are commonly produced by spinning, but unless a completely plain top is required, they may need profiling by hand. The simplest way to do this, particularly if there are a number of them, is to make a template. This can be developed and formed up from flat sheet or from paper. The template should fit inside the top of the vessel and its profile can be marked out with a scriber or a pencil. The top of the vessel is then cut to shape using curved snips and finished by filing.

Diag. VI:4 *Typical shape of the development of a jug with integral spout.*

Diag. VI:5 *Typical shape of the development of a separate spout.*

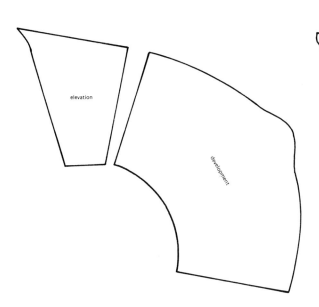

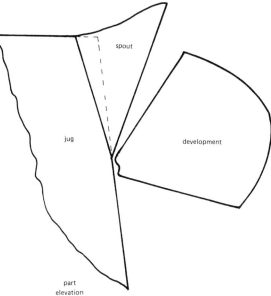

Fig. VI:29 *Profiled vessels with template in foreground, PMC Ltd. Sheffield.*

REPAIRING PEWTER

Every craftsman at some time will make a mistake and damage a piece of work in progress. If a lot of work has already been done on the piece, then a repair should be considered before discarding it.

The most likely repairs on new work are dents caused by dropping the piece, items that moved during soldering such as feet and handles, or burn holes and surface burns, which can occur very easily. With older pieces, again dents and bruises are the most common, but there will be a number of cases where feet or handles have been literally torn off, taking some of the metal with them.

Dents

Dents can be beaten and planished out using the techniques and tools previously described (pp. 53–6 and 64–8). In order to get at these dents specially shaped stakes may need to be made up, or purchased. If any are made up they should always be kept for possible further use.

Decorated areas need particular care in order to restore the decoration. Chased work needs to be beaten back out, beyond the original, so that it can be chased in again. It is not too difficult to rechase as most of the original work will still show and the original lines can be followed. Engraved areas are more difficult, as a lot will get lost in the beating out and reforming. Unlike chasing where the repaired area can be rechased, it may be necessary with engraving to recut the whole design.

In order to beat out and reform the shape, it may be necessary to remove items such as feet, handles or hinges before starting work.

Unsoldering

In order to remove items such as feet and handles the soldered joint must be melted. The joint area must be cleaned, so that the exact run or form of the joint can be seen. The work should be supported so that the main body or the appendage can fall away easily. For example, to remove a handle it may be found easier to hang the vessel over a hook or piece of wood by the handle. A soft pad of cloth, or a sandbag, is then positioned a short distance below the vessel so that it can fall safely. The joints around the handle should be fluxed, just as if the joint was to be soldered. The gas torch should be set to a very fine flame and, initially, the area around the joint and the handle should be warmed. The flame can then be directed at the original joint and as soon as the solder begins to run, moved around the joint. As soon as all the solder is fluid, the vessel's own weight will pull it away from the handle. Feet and hinges can be removed in a similar manner.

If a seam has to be unsoldered, some tension is necessary to pull it apart. Pieces of string attached to part of the body, with the hand pulling the other part, or the judicious use of weights, can all suffice. It is important to clean and flux the seam before attempting to melt out.

Holes and cracks

Cracks can be filled in much the same way as soldering a seam. The crack must be scraped out clean with a knife, scraper or scriber to remove all traces of varnish and dirt. Flux is then applied and the crack soldered as if it were a seam.

Holes can be filled by letting in a piece of pewter and soldering it in, or by melting in small pieces of pewter. If the hole is large then the edges should be filed so as to give the hole a reasonable shape. A piece of pewter of the correct thickness is held under the hole and the shape scribed on it. The piece is then filed to shape and let into the hole such that it is a good fit. Flux should be applied quite liberally around the joint prior to soldering. The loose piece of pewter will need supporting in some way and this is best done with a thin sheet of asbestos taped to the inside of the vessel. As it is unlikely that the fit of the piece in the hole will be perfect, the solder should be applied so that it builds up and can be filed off afterwards. If the patch is in an obvious position, a very high-tin content solder will have to be used so that the joint does not show.

An alternative method is to cut the patch smaller than the hole and support it on a sheet of asbestos so that a gap appears all round the patch. The gap is then filled with very small snippings of pure pewter, well fluxed. Using a very fine flame the snippings of pewter are melted, thus closing the gap and bonding to the patch and the main body. As the pieces of pewter melt, more snippings may have to be added to ensure that the gap is well and truly filled. It is better to deliberately overfill the gap and file off the excess than to try to just close it. Small holes can be filled in a similar manner by just using snippets of pewter without a separate patch. It is also possible to puddle in molten pewter using a fine electric soldering iron to melt the snippets.

ANTIQUE PEWTER REPAIR

Correcting distortions

Before starting to correct distortions or in fact any repairs, see if you have in your collection a similar piece in good condition, and have it handy on the bench while you are working, so that you can compare the workpiece with it as operations proceed.

Distortions are most easily corrected if the metal is thoroughly warmed, so it is desirable to have available a controllable source of heat, such as a bunsen burner or a blow lamp. Alternatively, immersion for a few minutes in water which has been brought to boiling point will usually suffice, but the advantage of a flame lies in the ability to reheat the piece quickly so that the work can proceed with the minimum of interruption.

The tools required consist of a slim-shafted 'hammer' with the head made of a ball of lead or lead and pewter, which will have to be home made, a pigskin mallet, and pieces of various kinds of wood which can be shaped with a sharp knife, and a file to suit the particular job in hand. Oak is useful for dealing with thick moulded foot rims, whereas at the other end of the scale, cedar being soft, is useful, particularly where it is necessary to 'squeeze' a piece back into shape in a vice, as being soft, if appropriately shaped, it will not dent the metal. A piece of lead solder or plumber's metal 9 or 10 in. long is useful as the end can be turned at a right angle and hammered into any shape that is needed to remove inside dents near the base of a tankard or measure.

Dents in holloware can then be removed by tapping gently on the inside with the 'hammer' and corrected from the outside with the pigskin mallet, which will not bruise the metal. Grip the piece with the thumb on the outside where the correction is needed and you can then feel the blow of the 'hammer' on the inside, which helps to place the necessary blows accurately. By passing the fingertips lightly over the surface it is possible to locate slight dents or protuberances which the eye does not always see.

Distortions of foot rims should be corrected with a hard wood tool, with the 'business' end shaped to fit the job. The tool should be long enough to be held in position with the piece in the one hand, so that it can be given a sharp blow with the 'hammer'.

If the body of a piece of holloware is distorted, as distinct from merely dented, it should be examined very carefully before starting operations, to decide exactly wehre the distortions are. First to receive attention should be the strongest, usually the thickest, part. If the handle is distorted or bent sideways as is often the case where the lower terminal has been driven into the body, this should be treated first by warming the piece round the finial, and knocking up from the inside; the handle itself should then be examined, straightened and set at the right angle to the body, before proceeding to the body. If the foot rim is distorted, this should be dealt with next as indicated above, and then the body can be tackled.

Some dents in holloware are caused or contributed to by the metal having become very thin due to wear and continual cleaning. They need careful treatment. Try to identify these by finger pressure from the inside before using tools, and then proceed with appropriate caution. It is possible to gauge the thickness roughly by gentle fingertip touch, one finger inside and one outside.

Examine carefully the curve of the handle – do not attempt to strike direct blows from inside the curve of the handle, or you will probably damage the body. Use a long wooden 'tool' and strike first from one side and then the other until the curve is correct. Some solid strap handles will answer to pressure from fingers and thumb, but distortions near the bottom joint will need the attention of a wooden striking tool. Never attempt to 'lever' out distortions, or use a wedge, as it is very easy to damage the body. Do not try to 'pull out' distortions in handles or you may pull the handle off the body.

Distortions of rims of flatware can often be dealt with by pressure of finger and thumb. A small anvil or a thick piece of iron with a smooth flat surface is useful. An old flat iron, gripped by the handle in a vice serves very well, but see that the surface is smooth and polished. Use the pigskin mallet to flatten the piece where possible. Some sharp dents may need the attention of a wooden tool.

STANLEY SHEMMEL

THE INDIVIDUAL APPROACH

The foregoing text has indicated the range of work that can be produced by using normal metalworking techniques and relatively simple tools.

Pewter, however, is unique in that its low melting point, softness, ductility and general ease of working does allow for an innovative approach beyond and in addition to the normal hand working of metal. Using a combination of both metal and woodworking techniques, it is possible to produce work in pewter that is quite unique to that material and which cannot be easily copied in other materials.

It is unlikely that this individual innovative approach is viable for high output, but it does give considerable scope to the individual craftsman with flair to develop work that is both unique and recognisable.

One such craftsman is Tom Neal and some examples of his work and techniques are given below to indicate the possibilities of his unique and unorthodox approach to the craft.

Bandsaw work

Pewter saws very easily and using the technique of bandsawing, as for wood, similar pewter forms can be produced. The pewter is cast into blocks by casting into simple moulds as explained elsewhere in the book. The cast block is then sawn as if it were a

Fig. VI:30 *A bandsawn flower holder, Tom Neal.*

Fig. VI:31 *Showing two cores and castings, Tom Neal.*

Fig. VI:32 *The process of flame sculpturing, Tom Neal.*

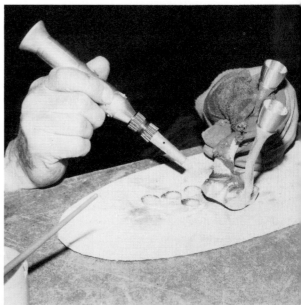

block of wood to the desired profile. The centre can be sawn out by going in through one corner and profiling the inside, the corner being soldered up afterwards. The saw blade gives a textured finish which can be left without further work. Variations of saw blade teeth pitch and band speed give variations of textured finish.

Dip casting

A variation on normal casting techniques is the innovative approach of dip casting. A metal core is turned or machined to the desired inside profile. The core can be of any metal, but pewter itself is ideal as it is available in the workshop and can initially be cast into a block prior to machining.

To produce a casting, a pot of pewter is heated until just fully molten and the cold metal core, which should be brushed with talc as a release agent, is dipped in. The molten pewter freezes on to the core and when the desired wall thickness is obtained, the core and the casting is withdrawn. Obviously considerable experience by trial and error is required to determine the parameters of draw angle on the core, size of core relative to molten mass, melt temperature, etc. Once this experience is gained, the technique opens up a wide range of possibilities. The outside of the casting can be left as cast, textured by wire brush or machined. If the core is designed to be held in a chuck, the casting can be taken from the casting pot directly to the lathe for turning before being removed from the core.

Flame sculpture

A variation on the normal technique of sculpturing is to use a technique known as flame sculpturing.

A very fine blowtorch is used to melt away the pewter from the surface of the article. The casting or block is held on or over an asbestos pad and liberally coated with a glycerine soldering flux. The pencil flame of the blowtorch is applied to the surface and molten pewter allowed to run off on to the asbestos pad. Like all techniques, considerable skill is required, and this can only be established by trial and error. Once this skill is achieved, a wide range of attractive and unique work is possible.

SUMMARY

The examples and techniques shown indicate the range of options open to the individual craftsman who is prepared to move away from the traditional techniques and processes and develop his or her own approach.

Pewter is an ideal material for trying out new techniques and processes, as there is virtually no waste. Spoiled or experimental work is simply returned to the melting pot for re-use.

Fig. VI:33 *Flame sculptured box, Tom Neal.*

VII Spinning and Spunware

SPINNING

Spinning is a metal-forming technique by which flat sheet can be easily formed into hollow vessels. The technique is fairly common in industry in general, but is of particular interest to the pewter-manufacturing industry. It has in the main replaced the hand methods of raising a hollow vessel and has allowed the industry to produce in large quantities. It has over the years also replaced a lot of cast pewterware, as spunware is generally cheaper because the metal is thinner and the items are quicker to produce. However, spinning should not be regarded only as replacing casting or hand work as it is a genuine technique for producing interesting and exciting articles in its own right.

Equipment

Lathe

The first requirement is a suitable lathe, preferably designed for the purpose. A heavy-duty, wood-turning lathe can be used as it is similar to a spinning lathe with regard to headstock, tailstock and tool rest. An engineer's lathe is not suitable except for small light work as it does not have the centre height required, and its bearings are designed for different forces than those applicable to a spinning lathe.

The lathe consists of a headstock to the left with a spindle mounted in large bearings, the nose of the spindle being threaded. A movable tailstock is on the right, and an adjustable tool rest is clamped to the lathe bed. The tool rest has a number of holes to accept one or more steel pins. A rotating or live centre is an essential requirement for the tailstock.

Chucks

The formers or chucks are machined to suit the shape of the article required. The chucks can be made from wood or metal or, more recently, plastic materials such as nylon. If wood is used, then it must be close-grained hardwood such as beech, boxwood, birch or maple. Soft-grained wood will not work to a fine finish and consequently marks

will show on the inside of the vessel. Metal chucks can be made from brass, cast iron or steel and can be polished to give a fine finish to give a good surface to the inside of spun vessels. Nylon is easy to machine and can be polished to a fine finish. It does not distort as some wooden chucks do, and it has a slight flexibility which metal chucks do not have. This gives a better grip and the slight flexibility like that of the wooden chucks gives a feel to the work when spinning.

Chucks can be internally threaded to suit the male thread on the lathe spindle, or alternatively can be mounted on separate false noses by means of wood screws or set screws through the flange of the false nose. A common method of internally threading wooden chucks is in fact to cast the internal thread using pewter. The first step in this process is to machine a copy of the lathe spindle nose from a

Fig. VII:1 *Spinning lathe, Charles Taylor Ltd.*

Fig. VII:2 *A selection of spinning chucks, James Dixon & Sons Ltd. (opposite)*

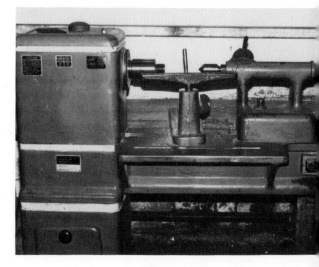

short stub of steel. A large hole is rough bored or cut with a wood chisel in the back of a part-machined wooden former. The stub mandrel is positioned centrally in this hole and molten pewter poured in. When the pewter is set and cold the stub mandrel is unscrewed, leaving a perfectly mating internal thread in the back of the wooden chuck. The chuck can now be screwed to the lathe spindle and turned to the correct form.

Wood and nylon chucks can be turned to the exact shape required on the spinning lathe itself using normal wood-turning tools and techniques. Metal chucks should be machined on an engineer's lathe using normal tools and techniques.

For vessels that require to be necked down, such as a shaped goblet, segmented chucks are required. These are relatively complex, and consist of a number of segments which fit together over a parallel shaft which is part of the chuck. The segments are designed so that the finished vessel is slid off the parallel shaft complete with segments which then fall loose and are removed individually. It is absolutely essential that a segmented chuck be built very accurately so that the joint lines of the segments do not transfer as grooves or ridges to the inside of the vessel. Alternatively, certain vessels can be formed on chucks that are joined in sections on the longitudinal axis so that the parts of the chucks can be removed from each end of the vessel. This usually demands that one end of the vessel, the base end, is cut off at the final stage in order to remove the chuck. A number of follow blocks are required of different diameters, with flat and hollowed faces to suit the form and size of the spun vessels. The follow block is mounted on a rotating centre in the tailstock and is used to clamp the pewter disc to the chuck.

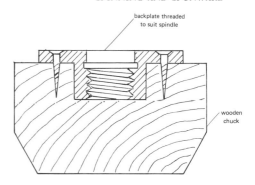

Diag. VII:1 *Hardwood chuck with backplate.*

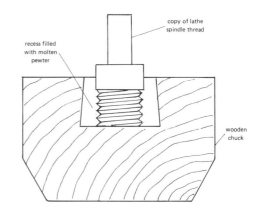

Diag. VII:2 *Hardwood chuck with cast pewter thread.*

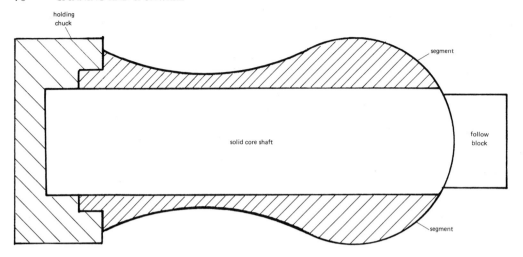

Diag. VII:3 *Section through segmented chuck.*

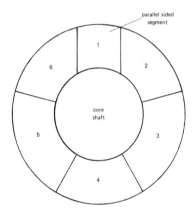

Diag. VII:4 *Section through segmented chuck.*

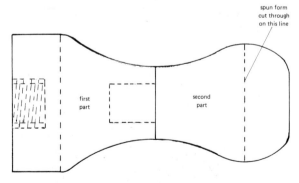

Diag. VII:5 *Joined chuck showing the two parts and position of cutting line.*

Forming tools

Forming tools are relatively large as the forces involved in spinning are high and the tool must be held firmly. Consequently, the tools are about 60 cm (2 ft) long, half the length being the wooden handle. The remainder is a steel shaft approximately 2 cm ($\frac{3}{4}$ in.) diameter forged to a shaped end. The shape of the end is determined by the spinning operation requirement.

A number of shapes and forms have been developed over the years, but most spinners seem to work with a range of five or six forms for the majority of the work. The most common forms are the spade end which splays out at the end and is slightly rounded on one side and flatter on the other, used for general forming, smoothing and burnishing. A hooked end tool of relatively large diameter, used for initial forming and drawing down. A ball-end tool for drawing down and forming. A smaller hooked end tool for returning an edge internally. A pointed end tool for turning an edge. A trimming tool with a sharpened edge for cutting away any surplus metal, usually smaller than the others and often made from an old file. Apart from the trimming tool, all of the tools are well rounded-off and polished smooth with no sharp edges to mark the work. The trimming tool is also used to cut decorative circumferential lines in work as the design requires.

Spinning and forming

If the form of the finished piece is relatively shallow and simple, the final chuck can be used for the complete process. More complex forms and deep forms are usually started on a first stage drafting chuck and then via a second or third stage chuck to the final form.

The circular disc of pewter is first lightly clamped between the chuck and the follower block

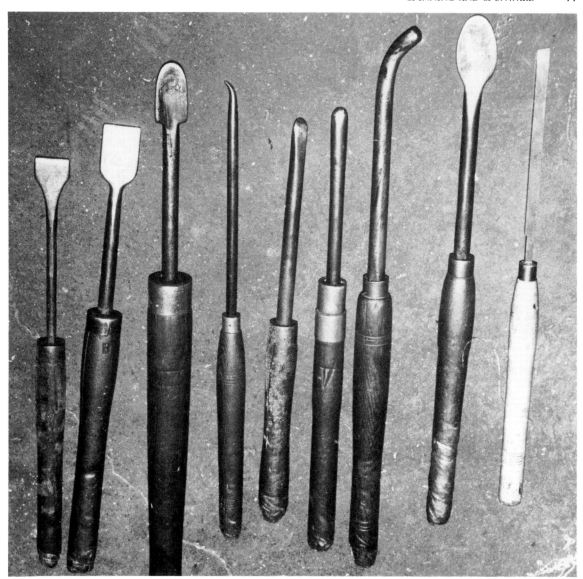

Fig. VII:3 *A selection of spinning tools, James Dixon &*
Sons Ltd. From left to right: trimmer, spoon burnish, large
hook, ball end, chisel end, small hook, spade burnish and two
straight burnishes.

Fig. VII:4 *Centring the disc of pewter on the lathe, Tether*
Manufacturing Ltd.

by pressure from the tailstock. The disc is centred
approximately by eye and the lathe started. If the
lathe has two or more speeds it is advisable to use a
lower speed of about 700 rpm at this stage. The
highly skilled professional spinner, however, usually
carries out this operation at the more usual spinning
speed of about 1,200 rpm. The disc is centred by

applying pressure to the edge with a stick of hardwood levered back against the tool rest. When the disc is running as true as possible the tailstock is screwed in to clamp the disc firmly between the follower block and the chuck, and if necessary the trimming tool is used to make the disc truly concentric. The follower block is chosen to suit the vessel requirement in diameter and end form, that is if a rounded end vessel is being formed, then a small diameter follower with a hollow face is used.

Before starting to form the piece, some form of lubricant is applied to the face of this disc. A number of lubricants are used, depending very much on the personal experience and views of the professional spinner. Light grease, oil, beeswax, tallow or beeswax and oil mixture are common lubricants and all seem to suffice. However, in a cold workshop tallow can give problems as it is rather hard and with pewter it is possible to force small hard pieces of the tallow into the surface of the vessel. It is preferable therefore to use one of the other lubricants.

The tool rest is adjusted such that it clears the disc and its height is below the centre line of the chuck. The tool, in this case the large hooked tool or rounded end tool, is tucked well in under the right arm. The peg is positioned in a hole in the tool rest to the right of the disc. The spinning tool is positioned between the peg and the disc, so that the peg acts as a fulcrum. The end of the tool is positioned slightly below the centre line of the disc. The spinner's left hand is positioned against the end of the tool rest, at the same time holding a wooden stick called a backstick. Using the pressure of the

body, the spinning tool is pressed against the disc by levering against the peg. The backstick is pressed firmly against the back of the disc to counterbalance the thrust of the spinning tool. The spinning tool and backstick are now moved in unison so that the pewter disc is gradually forced back over the chuck, the backstick preventing the edge of the disc from buckling. The disc is worked with short strokes of the tool with an occasional full sweep to prevent buckling until it is beginning to form a shallow dish. At this stage effort is concentrated on the base form of the vessel and the base drawn in over the chuck. Having set the base form, the remainder of the disc may now be drawn in.

It is sometimes necessary to carry out a trimming operation at this stage to clean and true the edge. For drawing in and final forming the first tool is exchanged for the spade-end tool or similar, using its rounded face. The tool rest is reset closer in and parallel to the chuck. The pin is repositioned to the right of longitudinal centre of the work piece so that the tool can move in a slight arc and cover a reasonable length of the vessel. The forming tool is positioned at a steeper angle than before so that it is acting in the lower quarter of the chuck.

The tool can now be worked back and forth over the metal, gradually forming it to follow the profile of the chuck. The spinner's left hand is used to

Fig. VII:5 *The first stage of spinning, using a large hooked tool and a backstick, PMC Ltd. Sheffield.*

Fig. VII:6 *The second stage of spinning, drawing in the base, PMC Ltd. Sheffield.*

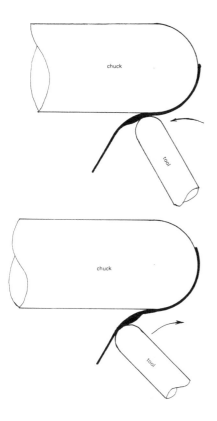

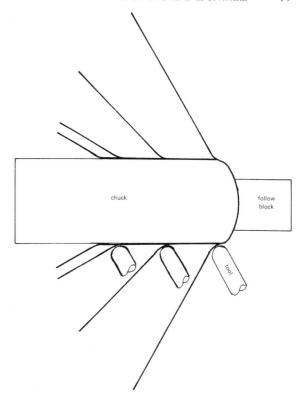

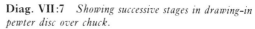

Diag. VII:6 *Moving metal back to regain thickness.*

Fig. VII:7 *The third stage, drawing in and final forming, PMC Ltd. Sheffield.*

Diag. VII:7 *Showing successive stages in drawing-in pewter disc over chuck.*

Fig. VII:8 *Final forming of the base, having removed the follower block, PMC Ltd. Sheffield.*

counterbalance the spinning tool, check the form for ridges or grooves by feeling with thumb and finger, and to apply further lubricant if required.

During this act of final drawing in and forming, the spinner's skill becomes very evident. The pewter flows in front of the tool almost like a wax. If the spinning tool is only pushed in one direction there are two dangers: the metal may be thinned excessively or, if taken to the extreme, torn away from the base form. The art is to move the metal as well as shape the vessel. Certain vessels demand that the metal be thickened up in places to suit the design and construction. For example, a goblet will have a much better appearance and appeal if the rim is thickened. This can be done by spinning the rim into a step before the final form is complete and then working the metal toward the rim end, thus thickening it up. Similarly, a jug or a pot can be thickened slightly in bands, by working from both directions, where the handles are to be attached.

Having finally formed the vessel against the chuck, the base needs forming to flow smoothly into the sides. The tailstock is removed, thus releasing the follower block. The tool rest is reset so that the fulcrum pin is in front of the chuck and the base of the vessel spun into the required shape, the spinner's left hand keeping the vessel in contact with the chuck if required, though normally the fact that the sides are already down keeps the vessel in place. The final stage is to burnish the vessel using the spade-end tool, this time with its flatter face to the work. The tool is used against the fulcrum pin as before, though lesser pressure is used, and run back and forth over the vessel to burnish out any spinning tool marks. A final trimming operation may be

Fig. VII:9 *High-form – (small diameter) – spinning showing disc, first and final stages, PMC Ltd. Sheffield.*

Fig. VII:10 *High-form spinning, showing the relatively small clamping area, PMC Ltd, Sheffield.*

required at the open end of the vessel. The completed vessel can now be removed from the chuck.

Spinning high forms

High forms are those where the height of the object is large relative to its diameter. For example, tall jugs or coffee pots, vases and stems of vessels. Over the years techniques have improved as have skills and it is possible to spin very high forms. However, the skill required is considerable, for in this form of spinning there is much more emphasis in making the metal flow over the former. In these cases sometimes two or three breakdown chucks are used gradually to form the shape. By the very nature of the shape the area of metal clamped between the chuck and the follow block is small and there is a high possibility of the metal tearing apart at this point. Once the technique is mastered, however, the satisfaction of producing such a piece is very great, and some beautiful designs can be produced.

Spinning on air

For vessels that neck down the use of segmented chucks has already been discussed (pp. 74–6), but it is possible to neck down or spin back in by spinning on air. The vessel is spun in the normal manner on a chuck to create the form required to the point where it necks in. At this stage it is removed from the chuck which is exchanged for a smaller diameter chuck that will pass through the neck. Spinning is carried out as before, but the

Fig. VII:11 *Some completed examples of high-form spinning, PMC Ltd, Sheffield.*

Fig. VII:12 *An example of high-form spinning on air from orginal flat disc, PMC Ltd, Sheffield.*

pressures are less and the whole operation more gentle as the vessel is necked down to the required shape on air. If a number of pieces have to be produced it is essential to work to a template as there is no chuck to give repeatability.

Rolling an edge

Many spun articles require a rolled edge, either rolled externally or internally. These edges are common on tankards both on top and bottom, porringers, bowls and similar items. If an edge is required by the design the basic metal disc needs to be cut at least 12 mm ($\frac{1}{2}$ in.) larger in diameter than the disc for a similar vessel without an edge. If the edge is to be rolled externally, the vessel can be spun normally and then a flange worked up at the end. This is done by using a small pointed tool and a small backstick. Using the tools in unison the flange is worked up square with the vessel. It is then carefully trimmed to give a good clean edge. Then using the backstick as a tool so that it is applied with upward pressure from below the centreline of the vessel, the edge will start rolling back. Continue until the edge is beginning to roll over then, using the spinning tool levering against the fulcrum pin, roll the edge back on itself. By the use of specially shaped tools the returned edge can be formed so as to be concave or flat or angular to suit its design purpose. If an internal rolled edge is required, then the vessel must be removed from the

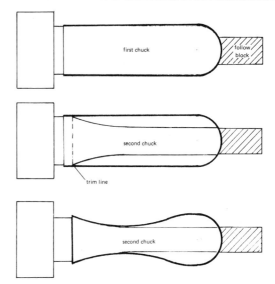

Diag. VII:8 *Second chuck used to neck-in vase.*

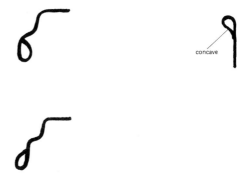

Diag. VII:9 *Rolled edges for tankards.*

main form chuck and remounted backwards against a chuck machined to suit the base of the vessel. A follower block of small diameter is used to clamp the vessel against the base form chuck. It is essential to check that the assembly is running true before commencing to roll the edge. The edge of the vessel is now virtually running in free air and the techniques of spinning on air applies (see pp. 80–1). Using a pointed tool the edge is gently folded back in until sufficient land is formed to roll. The trimming tool is applied carefully to trim to what will now be a hole concentric with the vessel. A small hooked spinning tool is now used to roll the edge back in and under. The tool rest and tool are operated in front of the vessel for this operation.

Other uses

The spinning lathe can be used for work other than true spinning. Hand-formed cylinders or rings such as napkin rings or box forms can be trued up, trimmed and decorated with circumferential grooves or lines. A chuck or mandrel should be turned to suit the diameter of the ring or cylinder and slightly tapered so that the ring can be slid on up the taper to a tight fit. The application of cold water by use of a brush or a rag is sufficient to cause the pewter to contract and become firmly fixed on the mandrel. The ring or cylinder then can be worked on with the spade-end burnisher and trimming tool to suit.

SPUNWARE

Tankard

The most common item of spunware is the tankard. Whilst these vary in size, proportions and shape, the great majority of tankards produced today are of the straight-sided conical form.

Body

The body of the tankard can be spun from a large circular disc or, alternatively, it can be formed from a developed flat sheet which is then rolled until the edges butt. The edges are then soldered together to form a seam. Most spun tankards in the UK are produced by the latter method, i.e. with a soldered seam, whilst it is common practice in the USA to produce from a large disc.

If a large disc is used, then this is clamped

Fig. VII:13 *Working up a flange prior to forming a rolled edge, Tether Manufacturing Ltd.*

Fig. VII:14 *Showing the flat disc and a finished base for the tankard, Tether Manufacturing Ltd.*

Fig. VII:15 *Spinning the tankard base, Tether Manufacturing Ltd.*

between a tapered chuck and a flat-ended follower. The disc is spun down over the tapered chuck until the shape and finish is attained. The end, which in fact is now the top of the tankard, is cut off with a trimming tool and there remains a seamless frustrum of a cone.

For a seamed body the developed shape, usually precut by the material supplier, is rolled around a tapered former by hand until the edges butt. The seam is now soldered using a high-tin, lead-free solder. The soldered seam is hammered down using a planishing hammer on a steel stake or former. The body is now slipped over a tapered chuck on the spinning lathe and using a spade-end tool the body is smoothed and burnished to shape, and if required decorative rings are cut in. A trimming cut is taken at each end of the body to square-off the ends and attain the desired length. The chuck is changed for a similar tapered chuck, but shorter so that the body overhangs the end of the chuck. This is to provide space and material for the top edge to be rolled back onto itself. Using a pointed tool and a backstick, a flange is worked up to suit the dimension required by the design. If necessary a slight trimming cut is taken to ensure that the edge of the flange is running concentric with the body. Again, using the pointed tool and the backstick, the flange is rolled back until the edge is in firm contact with the body. Once the rolled edge is formed it can then be shaped to suit the final design, which on drinking vessels is commonly concave.

Base

The base is formed from a disc of pewter again usually purchased precut to size. The exact size disc for commercial work can only finally be determined by trial and error. However, a rough approximation for a starting point is to project the design down to a straight line to find an approximate diameter. Add 12mm ($\frac{1}{2}$in.) for a rolled edge if it is to be rolled externally, or 18mm ($\frac{3}{4}$in.) if it is to be rolled internally.

Base with external rolled edge. The chuck is machined to the exact shape required and a follower block machined to suit the flat area of the base. The disc is clamped between the chuck and the follower block and using a round-nosed tool the base is formed over the chuck. A flange is worked up from the left towards the tailstock using a pointed tool and a backstick. After trimming for concentricity the flange is rolled back over the sides of the base and spun in to make firm contact with the sides. The base is now complete and can be removed from the chuck. For this type of base all of the spinning takes place on the one chuck, using the minimum of

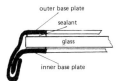

Diag. VII:10
Glass bottom for tankard.

material. However, the rolled edge is very apparent as it can be seen when looking down on the tankard, unlike the top edge which is rolled back under. A better quality alternative is to roll the edge internally, but it does use more material and demands a second spinning operation, thus making it more expensive to produce.

Base with internal rolled edge. The first stage is similar to that of the internal edge base, though the disc is larger in diameter. The disc is spun over the chuck as before, but instead of a flange being worked up the spinning continues to provide a shaped base with short parallel sides. The base is removed from the chuck and a second stage chuck is mounted on the lathe. This chuck is machined internally to exactly suit the shape of the base. The follower block is considerably smaller in diameter than the base to allow room for the spinning tools to roll in the edge. The base is clamped between the follower block and the chuck and the parallel sides are then spun in to form a flange inside the base. The hole thus formed is trimmed for concentricity, and using a small hooked tool the edge is rolled back inside. This gives a good appearance to the base compared with the external rolling, but does involve a second operation and a virtual spinning on air process.

Glass-bottom base

An alternative base is a glass bottom. A base is formed as previously described for an internal rolled edge base. Prior to removal from the chuck, the centre is cut out from the base with the trimming tool, leaving a land of approximately 10 mm ($\frac{3}{8}$ in.). A disc of pewter is cut to size so that it just fits inside the base. This disc also has its centre removed leaving an annulus 10 mm ($\frac{3}{8}$ in.) wide. A disc of glass is cut to fit inside the base and the glass is sandwiched between the inside of the base and the annular ring. A sealing medium of a food quality rubber mastic is placed between the glass and the base and between the glass and the annular ring. The whole assembly is mounted on the same internal chuck as used previously to roll the internal edge. The follow block clamps the assembly tightly together. The edge of the base is rolled internally until it makes hard contact with the annular ring, thus firmly clamping the glass in position. After removal from the chuck, surplus sealant is cut away leaving a clear glass bottom.

Final assembly

The body of the tankard is now soldered to the base and the whole given a polish and buff. The handle which is normally a slush casting is then soldered into position.

Georgian-style tankard

This style of tankard is of three-piece design, body, base and handle. The body is spun from a single large disc and formed initially over a parallel-sided breakdown chuck, which gives the final base shape but leaves the sides parallel. The body is now placed onto a segmented chuck and spun into the necked-in form. During the spinning operation the metal is manipulated to flow toward the rim to thicken it up slightly. The body is burnished with the spade tool and the rim is cut square with the trimming tool, thus completing the body. The body is removed from the lathe complete with segmented chuck which can now be removed piece by piece after the central core is removed. The base is initially a straightforward low form spinning on a single chuck of desired shape. After spinning to shape and burnishing, the follow block is removed and the centre of the base cut out with the trimming tool. The base is then fitted into an internal chuck and clamped with a follow block of somewhat smaller diameter so that the edge can be rolled internally in a manner previously described. The base is soldered to the body and the assembly so far is polished and buffed. The handle which has been cast and polished is then soldered into position. A final polish of the assembly completes the tankard.

Bowls and porringers

These items are of low form spinning and are produced in a large range of sizes of diameters and heights and subtle variations of shape and decoration. The spinning technique is, however, similar in all designs. Only one form chuck is used and all are produced from discs of pewter of suitable diameters and thicknesses.

The disc is clamped between the chuck and the follow block, which is usually concave to suit the form of the chuck. Three main spinning tools suffice for the major work on these items, the large hooked tool, the spade burnisher and the trimming tool. The disc is worked over the form chuck using the large hooked tool. After forming, the spade tool is used to smooth and burnish the vessel. The edge of

Fig. VII:16   *A completed tankard, Tether Manufacturing Ltd.*

Fig. VII:17   *Fitting the segments of the second-stage chuck, PMC Ltd, Sheffield.*

the bowl is cut square with the trimming tool, after which the edge is worked back to form a flange prior to rolling back. A small pointed tool in combination with a backstick is used to roll back the flange to form a rolled edge for stiffness and finish. After rolling back the edge, the roll is often worked on further to make it concave. This makes the appearance somewhat neater, particularly on heavy gauge material. Before the bowl is removed from the chuck, decorative line work can be cut into the bowl with the trimming tool.

Porringers have their base form slightly flattened, so that they stand square and steady. Most bowls, however, have a foot fitted. This foot is spun up in a similar manner to that described for the base of a tankard. The edge is rolled either internally or externally and prior to removal from the chuck the centre is cut out with the trimming tool. The foot is then soldered to the bottom of the bowl and the whole polished and buffed.

Sugar bowls

These are made in two basic parts, a base and a top soldered together.

Base

A form chuck of final shape is fitted to the lathe and a disc of pewter clamped to it with a follower block of concave form to suit the chuck. The disc is centred and using a large hooked spinning tool the

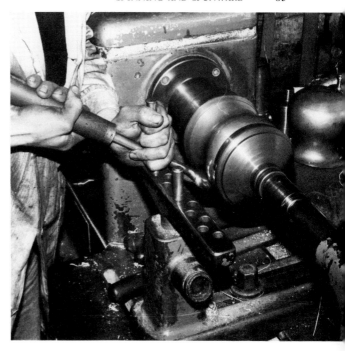

Fig. VII:18 *Burnishing the body on the segmented chuck, PMC Ltd, Sheffield.*

Fig. VII:19 *An example of a spun bowl, PMC Ltd, Sheffield.*

metal is formed to follow the form of the chuck. After forming, the edge is cut square with the trimming tool, the edge being left in the form of a small flange. The follower block is removed and using the spade tool the hemispherical base is formed to final shape and burnished. During this operation, the left hand is used to support the work.

Top

The chuck for this is a joined chuck. The disc of pewter is clamped to the joined chuck by the follow block and is spun to the desired shape using the large hooked tool. After shaping and burnishing, the follow block is removed and using a trimming tool the centre is cut out of the formed shape. The part-finished top is removed from the chuck and the right-hand portion of the joined chuck is also removed. The top is placed back on the remaining portion of the chuck, which is now shaped so that the edge of the top overhangs. Using a small pointed tool and a small hooked tool, the spinner rolls back internally the edge of the top.

The two parts are now finished and ready to be soldered together at the small flanges. Alternatively, bottom half shapes can be formed greater than hemispheres. This, however, calls for a second operation of spinning on air to spin the upper portion back in to continue the part-spherical shape. A foot similar to that described for the Georgian tankard can be fitted or alternatively a similar shaped cast foot can be machined and polished. Cast foot forms are heavier which helps with stability and are thicker and stronger than spun foot forms which need the edges rolled in for similar support.

Teapot

This is produced in a similar manner to that for the sugar bowl, though of course from larger discs. The bottom section being spun on a form chuck to give the hemispherical shape with parallel sides and then reversed and spun on air to complete the part-spherical shape. The top is as for the sugar bowl with a similar rolled in edge.

Coffee pot

The bottom part of the coffee pot is produced in the same manner as that of the teapot. The neck is a high form spinning, produced on a joined chuck, from a disc of pewter. After forming and bur-

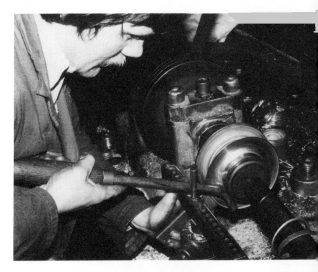

Fig. VII:20 *Trimming the edge, James Dixon & Sons Ltd.*

Fig. VII:21 *Spinning the top half of the sugar bowl (note the larger diameter follow block), James Dixon & Sons Ltd.*

Fig. VII:22 *Rolling back an internal edge for the top half of the sugar bowl, James Dixon & Sons Ltd.*

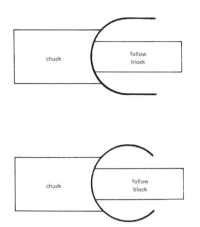

Diag. VII:11 *Spinning on air to form bowl shape.*

nishing, the form is cut through at the major diameter near the base. The base is discarded leaving the necked-down portion, the joined chuck being removed from each end as shown previously. The top section is soldered to the bottom using a turntable to aid soldering as explained previously (pp. 49–51).

Lids

Lids for the above items can be low form spinnings in one piece, or two pieces soldered together or, alternatively, a machined cast rim with a low form spinning soldered in a recess.

Fig. VII:23 *A completed sugar bowl consisting of a top spinning soldered to a larger bottom spinning, James Dixon & Sons Ltd.*

Fig. VII:24 *A completed spun coffee pot consisting of two major spinnings: a high neck and a bowl-shaped base. James Dixon & Sons Ltd.*

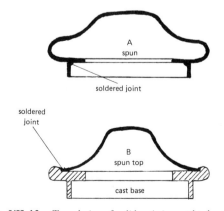

Diag. VII:12 *Two designs for lids: (a) completely spun, (b) spun top with cast base.*

Chamber candlestick

Three spun parts are used in the manufacture of this, plus of course the addition of a handle which may be cast or hand-formed.

Tray

The base or tray of this design is basically a low form spinning, though it has a deep parallel-sided set which demands some particular skill in spinning. The bottom of the tray is concave enabling it to stand well, so the follow block is machined convex to correspond. A suitable disc size is clamped between the follow block and the chuck and using a large hooked tool, the disc is spun in over the base form. The form then runs parallel for a short distance before the flange flares away. In order to form this section with its virtual 90° corner, it is essential to work an excess of metal back into this area before forming the relatively sharp corner. A pointed or small round-end tool is required to work the metal into this corner. Having formed the corner, the flange can be formed over the chuck and trimmed for concentricity. The edge of the flange is then rolled back on itself to form a rolled edge. Decorative lines can be cut on the parallel sides of the tray using a trimming tool. Before removing the tray from the chuck the exact concave form of the base is spun in after removing the follow block.

Candle holder

This is in two parts, an outer and inner. The outer is formed over a small chuck shaped to suit the final design and finished with a right-angled flange at the top end trimmed concentric. The bottom end is cut off square with a trimming tool. The inner portion is basically a top hat section with an internal diameter to suit the candle and finished with a flange some 12 mm ($\frac{1}{2}$ in.) larger in diameter than the flange of the outer portion.

The inner top-hat section is placed inside the outer and the assembly slid on to a chuck to suit the diameter of the outer. A follow block with a protrusion to suit the diameter of the inner is fitted into position. The tailstock is screwed in, thus clamping the two parts together, flange to flange. The larger flange of the inner is then spun back over the smaller flange of the outer, thus permanently clamping the two parts together. Final forming, line-scoring and burnishing can then take place to complete the part. The two major parts are polished and buffed and then the candle holder is soldered to the centre of the tray. The addition of the handle completes the candlestick.

CONCLUSION

The techniques, descriptions and illustrations in the text indicate the scope for the spinner, both student and craftsman. What cannot be described, however, is the feel for the material. This will only come by practice and experience. It is this feel that enables the craftsman spinner to make the operation look easy. It is the slight change in pressure, the slight vibration, the slight change in noise level or tone, the sensitivity of touch in the hand on the vessel which impart to the spinner information as to how the metal is flowing and forming. The reaction to this, by variation of pressure and stroke and angle of tool, produces the final article to the pewterers satisfaction. In a similar manner, experience determines the best spinning speed for a particular size and thickness of disc and whilst speeds quoted are in common use, the final decision is made by the spinner to suit his or her particular technique.

When this feel for the material is mastered along with the fundamental techniques, the spinner can produce the most beautiful articles for both decorative and everyday use.

Further examples of the spinner's craft are shown in the accompanying photographs, illustrating high form and low form spinning.

Diag. VII:13   *Moving metal back in to form sharp corner.*

Diag. VII:14   *Candlestick, showing candle holder rolled in.*

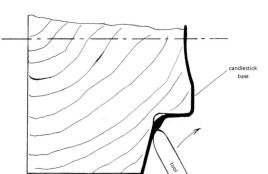

candlestick base

tool

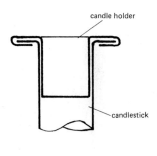

candle holder

candlestick

Fig. VII:25 *A spun chamber candlestick, PMC Ltd, Sheffield.*

Fig. VII:26 *A high-form spun coffee pot from a single disc, PMC Ltd, Sheffield.*

Fig. VII:27 *A low-form spinning from heavy gauge sheet, Gibson Pewter, USA.*

VIII Casting

INTRODUCTION

Casting is the oldest method of producing pewterware and in some countries, such as Germany, it is still the dominant method.

In America and the UK where spinning is predominant, and has been for many years, there is a gradual return to casting as techniques have improved or new techniques have been introduced.

Whilst casting into metal moulds is the traditional method of producing pewterware, there are a number of other methods in use, all of which will be described in the following text.

Pewter is an ideal metal for casting and, because of its low melting point and its very good flow properties, it is possible to reproduce very fine detail.

Over the years alloys have been developed to make the best use of the material and the numerous methods of casting. One of the most common alloys in use for casting has 92% tin, 7.5% antimony and 0.5% copper. Whilst other alloys are available, and in use, they are all low in copper compared with plate alloys. Good casting alloys melt at low temperatures, yet have a good working range so that they can be heated much higher for special work without detriment. They have a short pasty range for relatively 'sharp' cooling for good detail and have good flow characteristics.

MELTING POT

Common to all of the casting methods about to be described is the melting pot. Melting pots are available in a range of sizes and are usually made of cast iron. The heating medium is normally gas, either natural or LP gas, and for the temperatures required for pewter, natural draught burners are sufficient. A range of electrically heated pots is also available.

The casting alloy is supplied in ingots often shaped so that they can easily be broken into pieces for quicker melting and frequent top up.

Melt temperatures should be as the suppliers rec-

ommendation, which is generally about 55°C (130°F) above the liquidus temperature.

Once the pot is in use great care should be taken when topping up. It is absolutely essential that any top-up metal is absolutely dry. Any traces of moisture will immediately turn to steam and the violent expansion will throw molten metal out of the pot. This point should be borne in mind when remelting risers and sprues from previous castings which may have been quenched in water for final cooling. Top-up material can be kept alongside the pot or on top of a half cover over the melting pot to be sure that it is dry before use.

Dross can be minimised by using a flux. From time to time the dross should be skimmed off when it becomes excessive. The appearance of the dross and the surface of the molten metal gives an indication of the state of the melt. If it is blue-red-purple, the alloy is too hot. If it is lumpy, then it is too cold. A thin layer of dross is not harmful and will reduce oxidisation.

Different types of ladles are available in various sizes to suit the casting work in hand. Pouring ladles are either plain or fitted with a bridge piece behind the spout to hold back any dross on the surface of the metal in the ladle. Perforated ladles are designed to lift dross from the surface of the melt, the perforations allowing the pure metal to run out. Heavy gauge ladles are preferable.

When handling molten metal, protective clothing should be worn. Heat-resistant gloves should be worn as well as a strong canvas or leather apron and strong industrial safety boots or shoes. Lightweight comfortable safety goggles are cheap and easily available and should be worn at all times.

Moulds should stand on a firm bench in a clear space and there should be an unobstructed floor area between the melting pot and the mould.

If these normal precautions are taken along with good workshop practice, casting can be carried out in complete safety.

METAL MOULD CASTING

Gravity casting into permanent metal moulds is the traditional technique of producing cast pewterware. The technique has been in existence for hundreds of years, and even today the bulk of cast pewter is produced by this means.

Moulds

The moulds are made from cast iron, gunmetal or, latterly, steel and aluminium. Many that were made over one hundred years ago are still in daily use. The moulds are invariably bulky and heavy and consist of a number of pieces. Most of them are cleverly designed in the way that they lock together by the use of dowel pins, collars, caps and covers. The mating surfaces are an extremely close fit to prevent leakage when the molten pewter is poured in.

Examples of moulds are illustrated and show the method of construction. The mould for producing the body of a baluster is in four pieces. A heavy shaped base with a recess, into which fit two half sides, which in turn fit together with dowel pins. A recessed cap drops over a corresponding collar on the two sides, thus clamping the whole assembly tightly together. An even more complex mould is the one for the casket where the sides and end pieces are hinged together in such a manner that they can be wrapped around the central body. The top plate is then fitted on which clamps the whole assembly tightly together. The side pieces contain separate plates which carry the impression of the detail design.

The spoon mould is a simple two-piece mould fitted together via dowel pins and clamped tight with a G-clamp when in use.

Plate moulds are in two halves and are usually made from cast iron, machined to the desired shape. Alignment is by one half fitting into a recessed shape in the other half. The two halves are clamped together with two or more G-clamps. These moulds are very heavy because of their size and bulk, the large oval plate mould weighing some 40 kg (88 lb) when assembled ready for casting.

Before use these metal moulds require some form of coating on the cavity surface. Traditional coatings are paint-like mixtures of pumice powder, red or

Fig. VIII:1 *A four-piece metal mould for the top half of a baluster body, A. E. Williams.*

Fig. VIII:2 *Collapsible metal mould for a casket, James Smellie Ltd.*

Fig. VIII:3 *The two-piece spoon mould, A. E. Williams.*

yellow ochre and egg white or alternatively a mixture of black lead and graphite. The mixture is brushed on to a warm mould and allowed to dry. A number of coats are required to give a good surface cover, but if done correctly will last for many casts. Modern-day silicone sprays are available which are probably equally effective in reducing surface tension and avoiding flow lines.

With this type of mould it is rare to find, and difficult to incorporate, air release ways or vents and air must escape via the filling access or sprue. This technique is described later (pp. 104–5).

Castings produced from metal moulds are rarely finished as cast, and require machining and finishing processes before completion. Complex articles are usually cast in two or more pieces, which are then soldered together.

Casting

A common alloy for casting is one containing 92% tin, 7.5% antimony and 0.5% copper. However, different casters have their own preference based on tradition, experience and familiarity, and the alloys vary somewhat. At least two casters in the UK use an alloy of 98% tin, 1% antimony and 1% copper which produces excellent castings, but is probably more difficult for the inexperienced to use than the aforementioned alloy. Casting temperature is dependent upon the article being cast and the construction of the mould. Large area, thin section items, such as plates, may well require molten metal temperatures of up to 400°C (752°F) to give effective filling. Smaller and thicker section castings can be produced satisfactorily with temperatures at a little over 300°C (572°F).

Mould temperature is also relevant to the pro-

duction of good casting. Preheating can be done by placing the mould in an oven or by placing the mould on top of, or adjacent to, the melting pot. The usual practice is to finally determine the temperature by making a number of trial casts until good castings are produced. The rejects are simply returned to the melting pot.

The technique of pouring depends to some extent upon the shape and size of the mould. It is essential to avoid turbulence in the molten metal whilst filling and also to allow easy escape routes for the air. Consequently, with small moulds that can be held in the hand or rested on the bench and be easily moved by hand, it is common practice to pour with the sprue hole in a near horizontal position initially. The mould is then slowly returned to a vertical position, as the caster continues pouring, thus allowing the air and gases to escape via the upper part of the sprue hole. Once vertical, pouring is continued until the mould and filling aperture are full.

A suitable sized ladle should be chosen so that the pouring is completed in one operation without pause. If the ladle is too small and a second pour is required, it is highly probable that the casting will be flawed. The ladle should be dipped well below the surface of the molten metal in the pot so that it fills with good clean hot metal. Any dross picked up should be skimmed off just prior to pouring. Ladles can be coated with whiting to avoid scaling.

Fig. VIII:4 *Oval plate mould, A. E. Williams.*

Fig. VIII:5 *Pouring into a hand-held mould, A. E. Williams.*

Once the mould is full of molten metal, uniform cooling is required to give a good casting. If the mould is absolutely right with regard to shape and surface area, this may take place automatically. In practice this is unlikely and some deliberate cooling with a wet rag or a brush and water is required in critical places. These places are where the metal section is thickest and around the sprue inlet. This local cooling is necessary to prevent contraction cavities and surface blemishes. Experience and visual observation will indicate what cooling is required. Usually, very little is in fact required, quite often one brush stroke of cold water on the critical area makes the difference between a good and a poor casting.

When cooling is completed, the halves or parts of the mould are separated and the casting removed. This invariably demands the use of a 'knocker', which is a solid plug of soft metal, usually pewter itself, or hardwood, used to loosen the casting so that it can be prised out. The next stage is to saw off the sprues and feeders and then proceed with any machining and or linishing which will be described in the following worked examples.

Baluster measure

Casting

The body of the baluster is cast in two parts, a top half and a bottom half. The mould for the top half is in four parts, a base, two sides which fit together

Fig. VIII:6 *Releasing the casting (notice the pour marks on the casting), A. E. Williams.*

Fig. VIII:7 *The two halves of the baluster as cast, A. E. Williams.*

with dowel pins and a top plate which fits over the assembly and locks it together. In this particular mould there are two sprue holes and molten metal is poured into both holes at the same time using two ladles. When the metal is cooled and set, the mould is opened and the casting is removed using the knocker to vibrate it loose. The two sprues can be seen quite clearly, and also the pour marks on the surface of the casting.

The mould for the bottom is also in four parts, a base, two sides and a top. In this mould the sprue hole is through one of the sides and the metal is poured using the technique of starting with the mould near horizontal and gradually bringing it to a vertical position until the mould is full. After cooling, the mould is split apart and the casting removed as previously described.

The two halves are then ready for machining after the sprues have been sawn off.

Machining

The two parts are hand turned on a lathe, the most suitable being a spinning or a wood-turning lathe. The forces involved are relatively small, so a light duty lathe will suffice. A metal-turning lathe can be used, but for hand turning it is far from ideal as the area is congested by the saddle, top slide and tool post. Whichever lathe is used it should be fitted with a live or rotating centre in the tailstock.

The holding chucks and support or follow blocks are turned from wood to suit the shape of the casting. These shapes are invariably tapering in form and if a chuck is turned from hardwood, it will grip very well, especially if the casting is pushed on or tapped on with a wooden mallet.

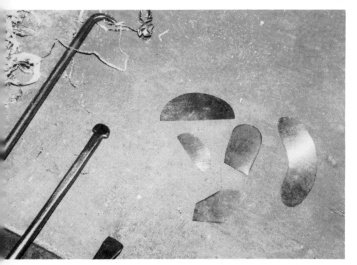

Hand-turning tools vary in size and shape to suit the job in hand, but are simple, being made from cast steel or silver steel hardened and tempered at the cutting end. The tool rest is a horizontal bar easily adjustable for height and position. The tool rest is positioned so that it is below the centre line of the casting to be turned and at such a distance away to allow complete manoeuvrability of the tool. The handle of the tool is held in the right hand whilst the left hand holds the tool on to the tool rest in such a manner that the tool can pivot both vertically and horizontally and also move backwards and forwards through the pivot point. Pewter is very soft and easy to turn but only light cuts should be taken to prevent the tool digging in. The tool is then manoeuvred to follow the form of the casting. The speed of the lathe is adjusted to suit the job in hand, but commonly with work of this size will run between 800 rpm to 1,200 rpm. With regard to the parts for the baluster, the inside form is turned first and finished to the desired shape. If touch marks are to be punched in it is usual to do this before completing the internal turning so that no bruises show on the inside.

When both parts have been machined internally they are soldered together to produce a complete body. This operation is best carried out using a turntable so that the work can easily be rotated during the soldering process.

The body is then returned to the lathe so that the outside surface can be turned to shape. This particular article is the type that will ring like a bell and is liable to do so whilst being turned, causing vibration or chatter marks from the tool. In order to prevent this the vessel is packed tight with cotton waste before being mounted on the tapered chuck. The vessel is supported by a follow block on the rotating centre in the tailstock. Turning is carried out as previously explained (pp. 93–4), the tool being manoeuvred to machine the whole surface. Circumferential grooves for decorative purposes are cut in at this stage.

The body is then linished or polished, depending upon the desired finish, and the handle is soldered on.

Fig. VIII:8   *Typical hand-turning tools and scrapers, James Smellie Ltd.*

Fig. VIII:9   *Hand-turning showing how the tool is held on to the tool rest, A. E. Williams.*

Fig. VIII:10   *Machining the inside of the body, A. E. Williams.*

Fig. VIII:11 *Packing the body with cotton waste to prevent vibration when turning, A. E. Williams.*

Fig. VIII:13 *Final turning of the baluster body, supported by a rotating follow block, A. E. Williams.*

Fig. VIII:12 *The completed baluster and candlestick, A. E. Williams.*

Large plate

The mould for this plate some 41 cm (16 in.) in diameter consists of two parts, a bottom and a top made from cast iron machined to shape. Because of their large diameter, plate moulds are also fairly thick to prevent distortion or breakage when in use.

Casting

The mould is supported on a wooden frame at an angle and clamped together with G-clamps. Prior to casting, the mould needs to be preheated, as with such a large bulk of metal and a large surface area, the heat loss from the molten pewter is very fast. For this type of casting, of thin section and large surface area, the temperature of the melt needs to be very high, at the top end of its working range, approximately 380°C (716°F) as opposed to approximately 300°C (572°F) for the baluster and the candlestick. With a plate of this size, it is also necessary to get the metal in fast, and in one operation, so two ladles are used. The metal is poured down the back of the sprue gate, so that it runs down the back of the angled mould, and then fills from the bottom up pushing the air back out through the sprue gate. It is common for one or two trial casts to be made before the mould reaches an ideal temperature and produces a good casting.

Once cast, the plate cools very rapidly because of the mass and area of the mould and is easily removed when the mould is opened.

Machining

The first step is to saw off the sprue and the plate is ready to be machined on the lathe.

In this particular case it was decided to use one of the castings as a former which was screwed to a large disc of wood, which in turn was screwed on to the lathe spindle. The former was then rough machined to the correct profile, and also to ensure that it was running concentric with the lathe spindle.

The plate was then soldered to the former by tack or stitch soldering around the edges.

The lathe is run at a much lower speed than with small items and with a plate of this diameter, $16\frac{1}{2}$ in., approximately 400 rpm is sufficient. The tool is held in a manner similar to that already described with the left hand being used to act as a pivot point.

When the plate is fully machined, using the tools, it can be smoothed off using the scrapers. Old machine hacksaw blades can be used to make scrapers which are easily ground and sharpened to a range of profiles.

Fig. VIII:14 *Casting the plate, James Smellie Ltd.*

Fig. VIII:15 *Opening the plate mould, James Smellie Ltd.*

Fig. VIII:16 *Showing the final plate stitch, soldered to the former which is screwed to the wooden face plate, James Smellie Ltd. (left)*

Fig. VIII:17 *Hand turning the large plate, James Smellie Ltd. (right)*

Fig. VIII:18 *Finishing the plate with an abrasive pad, James Smellie Ltd.*

After scraping, a satin finish can be applied using fine emery or carborundum paper or as in this case a soft abrasive pad. The plate is then removed from the former by cutting through the solder stitches.

A reversed former is fitted to the lathe spindle and the machining process repeated on the inside of the plate.

Upon completion of machining, the edge is finished by hand to remove traces of the solder stitches.

The plate is shown as finished from the lathe. It was, however, decided at a later date to reduce the machining marks still further. This was done by pressing the plate into a bed of clay on a potter's wheel, which solved the holding problem, and do further hand-finishing at high speed using a silicone carbide wet and dry pad.

Further examples of castware are shown.

SLUSH CASTING

Slush casting is a method of making hollow castings without the complexity of using cores, particularly where the profile or surface finish of the inside is relatively unimportant. This makes it an ideal method for producing handles, spouts, knobs, salt and pepper pots, small flasks and similar articles. It is also a useful technique in reducing the weight of a cast item such as a handle or knob or other attachment to a main article, where a solid attachment could upset the overall balance or feel.

The process consists of pouring molten metal into a metal mould and then pouring out the central volume of metal before it has chance to cool. This produces a casting which, whilst conforming exactly

Fig. VIII:19   *The plate finished, machined prior to further hand polishing, James Smellie Ltd.*

Fig. VIII:20   *Further examples of cast and machined-pewter antique finish, A. E. Williams.*

to the profile of the mould, has a relatively thin wall section and is hollow.

As the technique demands rapid cooling of the surface, metal moulds are essential for good performance. Gun metal or bronze has been shown to be an ideal material with the correct heat transfer rate. Cast iron can be used, but as its heat transfer is lower, the process is slower and the 'snap' cooling does not occur so readily, making it somewhat difficult to keep the walls relatively thin. Aluminium has the opposite effect, as its heat transfer rate is higher and unless the process is carried out very quickly, the whole mass can solidify. The time cycles of these last two materials are therefore difficult to gauge.

The alloy used has an effect, and an ideal alloy is one with near eutectic characteristics or a short pasty stage so the snap cooling at the surface occurs readily. Other alloys can of course be used, and this is particularly true of the spinners who use their off-cuts and rejects as the casting material for their handles and other attachments.

Moulds

The moulds are invariably two-part moulds, sometimes hinged to open like a book, and usually fitted with projections on each side to make them easier to hold.

Casting

The mould is held in the hand using a strong, thick

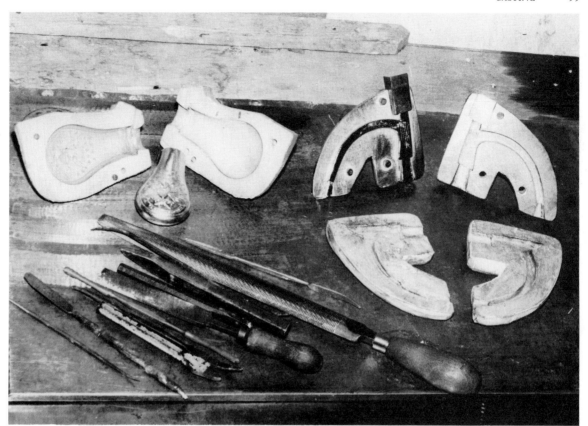

Fig. VIII:21 *Showing typical slush casting moulds, Tether Manufacturing Ltd.*

Fig. VIII:22 *Filling the mould, Tether Manufacturing Ltd.*

glove or cloth for protection. The mould must be preheated to give the correct casting conditions. When first starting to cast it is common practice to cast one or two items solid to bring the mould up to temperature. The solid casts are returned to the melting pot. There is no need for excessive heat and the melt should be at the lower end of its working range, around 300°C (572°F), depending upon the alloy being used.

Once the mould is at its working temperature the metal is poured into the mould and after a few seconds the mould is upended and the surplus molten metal returned to the ladle. The time before inversion of the mould can only be found by experience, as there are so many variables such as size and bulk of mould, temperature of mould, temperature of alloy, type of alloy, desired weight or wall thickness, that it is impossible to give exact detail data.

Once the surplus metal has been poured out, the

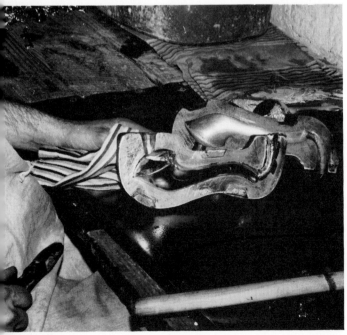

mould can be opened immediately and the casting removed and set aside to continue cooling.

The process is quite fast and outputs of one casting per minute can be easily achieved.

It is also possible to semi-automate this process, by clamping the mould in a fixture which can be tipped mechanically or pneumatically. The operator then fills the mould from a ladle, presses a foot pedal to invert the mould and catches the surplus metal in the ladle. This takes away the tiring work of constantly holding a heavy mould in the hand.

It is usual to give moulds of this type a very fine internal finish, highly polished or a mirror finish if possible, to reduce the amount of final polishing and buffing.

SILICONE RUBBER MOULD CASTING

The introduction of silicone rubbers has greatly eased the problems of producing small, finely detailed castings in pewter. These materials, known as Room Temperature Vulcanising (RTV) or Cold Cure (CC) silicone rubbers, are liquids which cure by catalytic action into tough heat resisting, yet flexible, materials. Because of their initial liquid state and final heat resistant flexible state, they are ideal for producing moulds of finely detailed and complex patterns. Their working temperature range is ideally suited to molten pewter (250°C to 300°C) and moulds can be reused many times.

Silicone rubber moulds are used in the pewter industry either in their own right as moulds for short runs up to 150, depending upon complexity, or as the initial mould to produce masters for centrifugal casting.

Models and modelling

The first stage is to produce a model or pattern for the future casting, or alternatively of course, existing patterns or models may be available. A word of warning is applicable here, as care must be taken not to copy existing models or figures if there is any possibility of them carrying a design copyright.

Models can be sculptured, or carved, from almost any material, wax, plasticine, plastic, plaster, wood or metal, as the silicone rubber being a cold compound will not affect or be affected by them. Alternatively, natural objects such as acorns, leaves or twigs can be used. If a master model is to be prod-

Fig. VIII:23 *Draining the surplus metal, Tether Manufacturing Ltd.*

Fig. VIII:24 *The open mould showing the finished casting, Tether Manufacturing Ltd.*

Fig. VIII:25
Materials and equipment for silicone rubber mould making, Trylon Ltd.

uced, then a sketch or drawing is usually the first stage, or if authentic modelling is the subject, then photographs and reference books will be required. It is usual to build the model around a wire or stick which gives support to the model, and, just as important, gives the modeller some means of holding it as work progresses.

Wax is an ideal medium for modelling and can be obtained in a number of grades of hardness, the most suitable being hard carving grade, or filing wax. The wax can be worked and smoothed to a very fine finish and be highly detailed. Special tools are available which give the modeller scope. Alternatively simple tools can be easily made up from lengths of silver steel or knitting needles or old dental tools. An advantage of wax is that if the first cast shows problems, then the master can easily be modified or reworked. It is also possible that once the master is completed, it can be seen that it is not mouldable in one piece, and in which case an arm or a leg may need to be cast separately. It is relatively easy to cut the piece off the master for separate casting and add pins or dowels for refixing at the final stage. Some other modelling compounds such as Milliput and Das are very useful as they initially work soft and air-harden in about 8 hours to form a very strong rigid model which can be filed or sawn for final detail.

Some points to remember when producing the model are, that large flat surfaces are difficult to cast and are better convex. Very deep undercuts are difficult to cast and even if these are suitable for silicone rubber, they could be less suitable for moulds used in centrifugal casting, as these moulds are less flexible. Very smooth surfaces are difficult to cast and can show up slight shrinkage marks, a textured surface is preferable. Parting lines must be borne in mind during modelling and if possible be incorporated in the design to fall in textured or in unobtrusive areas. Holes or openings should be smooth and the edges rounded off to ease demoulding and to prevent the rubber mould being torn. If dimensions are critical, though this is probably unlikely in figure models, statuary, handles, plaques, etc., then allowance must be made. It is extremely difficult to give exact figures because of the large number of variables, but an approximate guide is to allow 10% shrinkage between the original master and the final production model cast in a rubber mould. A final point is that the casting can never be better than the original master model!

Moulds

Moulds can be produced in three basic forms, split moulds, complete moulds cut after curing, or single-sided moulds. The most common form for figure models and shapes with undercuts, or complexities,

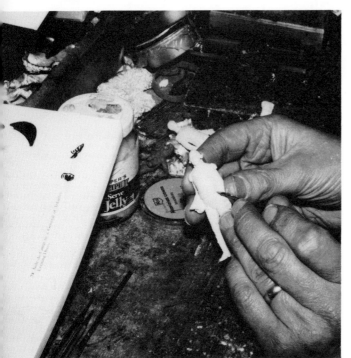

is the split form of upper and lower halves.

Split mould

A simple frame is required and this can be made from two strips of aluminium, each bent at 90° to form one short arm and one long arm. The width of the strip should be 25 mm (1 in.) wider than the thickest section of the model. This is so that there is at least 12 mm ($\frac{1}{2}$ in.) of silicone rubber all round the model. The short arms of the aluminium strip are cut to the same proportions. The two aluminium strips are laid on their edges on a perfectly flat surface, such as a piece of plate glass or an old plate-glass mirror, and adjusted to a suitable length. The length of this adjustable box should be approximately 40 mm ($1\frac{3}{4}$ in.) longer than the model to give space for the sprue header. Once positioned the aluminium strips can be held in position on the glass base by a fillet of plasticine. Alternatively, a

Fig. VIII:26 *Carving a wax model, Phoenix Model Developments Ltd.*

Fig. VIII:27 *Showing two halves of a silicone rubber mould, the original model and a casting complete with sprues, Phoenix Model Developments Ltd.*

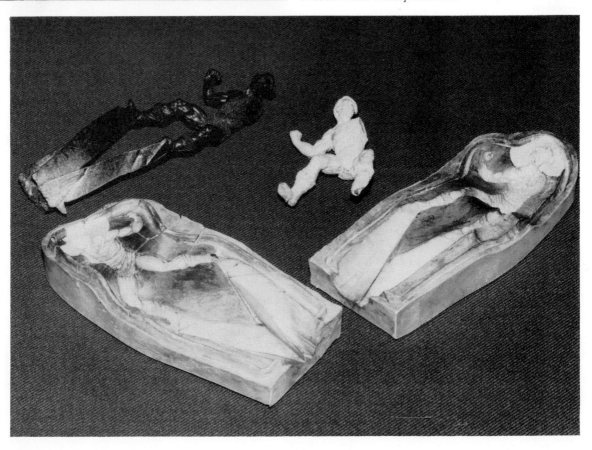

box can be built from Lego modelling bricks to any desired size.

The lower half of the box should now be filled with plasticine and the model or pattern pressed in to approximately half its thickness. The plasticine should be firmly pressed in around the model and the exposed surface smoothed off and contoured to suit the desired parting line. Keys should be inserted too, built up from plasticine, to act as alignments for the two halves of the mould. The exposed surfaces of the plasticine and box should then be coated with a release agent to prevent the silicone rubber sticking to them. Release agents are available commercially, but an effective agent can be made up from 2% petroleum jelly and 98% white spirit, mixed warm. The model itself, especially if made from wax, does not require a release agent, though if made from wood or plaster it should be coated with a sealant or shellac and wax-polished to give a good surface to the mould.

The silicone rubber should now be mixed according to the supplier's instructions. The mixing should be carried out in glass, ceramic metal containers or disposable plastic cups and the proportions quoted strictly adhered to. Too little catalyst is fatal as the rubber will not cure, so if there is any doubt, then err on the high side. Care must be taken in mixing so that the minimum amount of air is mixed in as the mixture is very viscous and air bubbles have difficulty in escaping. Once mixed, use a small paint brush to paint silicone rubber on to the exposed surface of the mould, especially in crevices and fine detail. This will eliminate air bubbles at the critical faces. Pour the remainder of the silicone rubber into one corner of the mould box allowing it to flow around the model. Pour slowly, to avoid trapping air and at about half full, pause slightly to allow air bubbles to break. Continue pouring until there is a minimum of 12 mm ($\frac{1}{2}$ in.) of rubber above the highest point of the model or to the top of the box if prepared as described. Silicone rubber is very expensive and once the catalyst is mixed, curing starts immediately, so only mix the desired volume as any excess can only be thrown away.

Once the mould is full, the silicone rubber must be left to cure. The curing time is dependent upon the rubber and the catalyst, and varies from 2 to 24 hours. Heat curing after setting improves the performance of the mould particularly with the initial casts in reducing bubbling of the cast surface. This information is of course provided by the supplier of the rubber and catalyst.

When the first half of the mould is cured, the box is turned over and the plasticine half removed

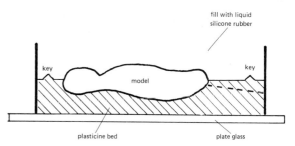

Diag. VIII:1   *Forming first half of silicone rubber mould.*

and discarded. Any rubber flash in the mould should be trimmed off at this stage. The mould should be carefully reset in the completed half of the mould and the finished surface of the mould coated with release agent or a thin coating of vaseline. This is essential, otherwise the fresh silicone rubber will stick. The top half of the mould is now poured as previously described and allowed to cure.

After curing, the two halves of the mould are separated and the model removed. The sprue runways can now be cut out using a very sharp modelling knife. Alternatively, sprues could have been moulded in along with the model by forming sprueways from wax and attaching them to the model. This method does in fact save valuable silicone rubber.

Complete mould

An alternative method of making a mould is to pour it in one operation and cut it open after curing. This is best done by standing the model vertically in a suitably sized box that will give a minimum thickness of 12 mm ($\frac{1}{2}$ in.) of rubber. The model should be attached to a sprue form of suitable size and then stood centrally in the box. The silicone rubber, mixed as before, is poured slowly down one corner of the box gradually rising up the figure until the box is full. After curing, the mould is removed from the box and is cut through to the model with a sharp modelling knife. It is preferable to only cut through on three sides, that is, one long side and top and bottom allowing the other long side to act as a hinge and the mould to open like a book. If the mould is cut right through, then there is some difficulty with realignment as this method of producing a split mould gives no opportunity to fit keys.

Open moulds

These are suitable for plaques, badges or castings having a flat back or base. In this case the model is placed directly on a flat surface surrounded by a fence, or box, and the mould produced as described previously.

For large plaques a considerable volume of sili-

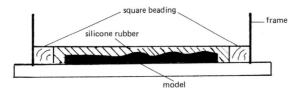

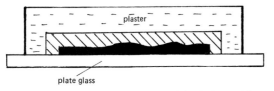

Diag. VIII:2 *Showing rubber mould, backed up with plaster.*

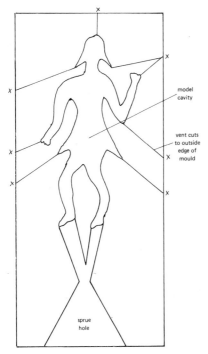

Diag. VIII:3 *Showing position of vents and sprue in rubber mould.*

cone rubber is required to give the mould sufficient rigidity for casting, so, in these cases, it is possible to minimise the volume of rubber and use a moulding plaster to complete the mould.

The pattern is placed on a flat surface as before and surrounded by a fence or box. A square beading of a thickness greater than the plaque is fitted around the inside of the box, leaving the plaque model inside a smaller box. The silicone rubber is prepared as before and poured over the plaque

model up to the level of the beading and allowed to cure. The beading is then removed, leaving the plaque model in its relatively thin mould in the centre of the box. A plaster mix is then made up from dental plaster or suitable commercial plaster and poured over the rubber mould until the box is full. Once the plaster has set and dried, the completed mould is ready for use. If possible, the complete mould should be left in the box for additional strength and to protect the plaster.

Casting

Prior to casting the new mould should be checked for cleanliness and rubber flash. Flash is carefully removed with a sharp knife. The mould should be examined for possible air locks, and vents cut where necessary. Vents are cut with a fine knife and taken to the periphery of the mould. Areas liable to airlock are sharp recessed corners and the extremities of the moulded shape.

The two halves of the mould should be dusted with talc or a mixture of talc and graphite. Excess powder must be blown, or tapped out, particularly in a mould with fine detail and undercuts. The mould halves are assembled and the whole clamped tightly together between two metal plates using a G-clamp. Clamping pressure must be sufficient to seal the mould, but not squeeze it, or else distortion of the mould will affect its accurate reproduction.

For a small mould, the metal can be melted in the ladle itself if no main source of molten pewter is available. Place small pieces of pewter, of a suitable casting alloy, into a ladle and melt using a gas torch. Once the metal has melted, scrape off the dross and continue to heat for approximately the same time as it took for the pewter to melt. Clear the dross once more and carefully pour the molten metal into the aperture of the mould. The mould should be supported at an angle of approximately 15° to the vertical and the metal poured down one side of the sprue opening so as to allow room for the displaced air to escape. Continue filling until the sprue is completely full. Tapping the mould will assist air bubbles escaping. After a few minutes the mould can be opened and the mould removed. Care must be taken, for at this stage the casting will still be very hot.

The first casting must be examined carefully for complete filling of the mould and, if necessary, additional air vents should be cut in. Alternatively, if the mould itself appears to be satisfactory then a second casting should be made with the metal brought to a higher temperature. The alloy should be one with a reasonable solidifying or pasty range, so that the metal has time to flow before setting off.

Open moulds can be filled simply by pouring the molten metal into the open back and satisfactory casts can be made. However, shrinkage does cause the back to set concave and any dross or dirt affects the surface. Considerable cleaning up is usually required, and allowance must be made to account for this in the design and dimensions of the pattern. A better method is to use a false back and cut a sprue way in the mould at one end. Then using the mould like a two-part mould the metal can be poured in a similar manner from one end. This gives a casting with a smooth flat back with the sprue and the dross being at one end and easily removed. The false back need not be made from rubber, and a suitable material is a heat-resistant refractory material, used by jewellers, called Supablock. This is easily sawn and filed and is very flat and smooth.

Press casting

An alternative method of casting in open moulds is press casting.

The open-topped mould is placed on a metal plate and pewter poured into the open mould. The pewter will remain proud of the top of the mould and by placing a hot steel plate on top to force the metal into the mould very fine detail can be achieved. The hot plate should be pressed down until the pewter has solidified. It is important that the hot plate is at a sufficient temperature to ensure that the pewter chills from the detail surface at the bottom of the mould, freezing last on the face of the hot plate so that no porosity occurs on the front face of the medallion.

Shock casting

An alternative method to this technique, which works well for small castings, is what might be termed 'shock' casting. Place the mould under a fly-press or similar tool which has a suitable flat-faced anvil attached to it. As soon as the mould is filled with pewter bring the anvil down sharply on top of the mould and hold under slight pressure until the pewter has solidified.

Fig. VIII:28 *The mould assembly ready for casting, J. A. Murrell.*

Fig. VIII:29 *Open top mould used in press casting: (note overflow wells in mould and fine detail in the casting), Hull Pewter.*

CENTRIFUGAL RUBBER MOULD CASTING

Rubber mould casting by the centrifugal method is, today, a very common method of producing small items quickly, accurately and to a high standard of finish and complexity.

Basically, an impression or impressions are formed in two thick circular sheets of rubber which are then clamped together. The top sheet has a central hole which connects with runways in the rubber which lead to the impressions, or cavities. Molten pewter is poured into the central hole of the top sheet whilst the mould is rotated at high speed. The molten pewter is forced along the runways into the cavities by the centrifugal force. When the metal has cooled, the two halves are parted and a radial display of cast parts are seen, each being connected to the central core by arms or sprues. The parts are cut from the arms and the central core and arms are returned for remelt. The rubber moulds are semi-permanent, of relatively low cost and quickly and easily made.

Moulds

The moulds are produced from sheets of unvulcanised synthetic rubber usually supplied in ready cut discs or sheet form. The discs are available in a range of diameters and thickness depending upon the items to be produced. Standard sizes are 150 mm (6 in.), 225 mm (9 in.) and 275 mm (11 in.) in diameter with thicknesses ranging from 12 mm ($\frac{1}{2}$ in.) to 18 mm ($\frac{3}{4}$ in.). The rubber also comes in various grades of hardness to suit the casting, ranging from soft for models with deep undercuts to

Fig. VIII:30   *Centrifugal casting machine, with integral melting pot, and discs of vulcanising rubber for making moulds, N. Saunders (Metal Products) Ltd.*

Fig. VIII:31   *Laying out a rubber mould, Phoenix Model Developments Ltd.*

hard for thin finely detailed castings such as filigree work.

The unvulcanised rubber disc is made up from a number of layers of rubber, each layer being approximately 2 mm ($\frac{1}{12}$ in.) thick, laminated together. The laminations can be separated if necessary, to suit the design of the mould, by warming the rubber or by the use of a rubber solvent. As the material at this stage is uncured, it does have a limited shelf life, less than a year, depending upon its formation. Consequently it should be kept away from sunlight and should be stored in a cool place.

Preparation and forming

Bring the two discs of unvulcanised rubber to room temperature and cut a hole in the centre of one disc in order that the metal may enter the mould. Usually discs are supplied with this hole preformed to suit the lower end of the funnel of the casting machine.

Layout

Take the models or patterns which have been made as previously described or use existing patterns. These patterns must be made of metal to withstand the temperature and pressure of the vulcanising process; pewter is perfectly suitable. Lay out the models on the upper disc so that there is ample room for runners and venting and ease of removal. Use a pair of compasses to centralise and space them equidistantly. The model should be positioned so that its best face is in the lower disc, as air bubbles and any dirt or dross will rise and therefore will be at the back or less important area of the model. Press the models firmly into the rubber disc until the desired parting line position is reached. Now fit a shaped former in the center so as to line up with the hole in the upper disc and form a basin in the lower disc. This basin and the corresponding hole feed the sprues or runners to the individual cavities. It is possible to use standard or pre-prepared sprue forms in metal, and also mould them in. However, as patterns vary so much in size and number per mould it is far preferable to cut the sprues to suit, after vulcanising. Locating nuts or pins must now be inserted to give mould half alignment. These nuts, or register pins, should be positioned nonsymmetrical so that the two halves of the mould can only go together one way. The lower half of the mould is then pressed down firmly on to the upper half.

Vulcanising

The two halves of the mould are now placed in the vulcanising frame, which is a ring to suit the diameter of the discs, a bottom plate and top pressure plate which fits inside the ring. The inside of the vulcanising frame must be coated with a release compound to prevent the rubber vulcanising to the frame. Wet compounds are available, as are silicone aerosol sprays. Parting compound must also be applied to the model and the two inner faces of the mould. Dry compounds such as molybdenum disulphide or fine powdered graphite are preferable and these also give a bright finish to the mould cavity. This is particularly important as the graphite prevents the two halves from being vulcanised together. It is also possible to line the upper and lower plates of the vulcanising frame with old newspaper, which acts as a release medium and, is claimed by some casters, to aid in gas release during the mould curing process. The vulcanising frame, complete with models, is loaded into the vulcanising press which has been preheated to the correct temperature. The presses available are both hand-operated, or hydraulic and the platens are heated electrically and thermostatically controlled. The vulcanising temperature varies, depending upon the particular rubber being used, this information being provided by the supplier. The normal temperature range for this type of rubber is between 154°C (310°F) and 185°C (365°F). Initially, only gentle pressure is applied as the rubber is cold, and excessive pressure would damage the models and the mould. After a few minutes the rubber will begin to become plastic and start to flow and then full pressure can be applied. On the hydraulic machine, this will be automatically controlled at approximately 0.7 kgf/mm^2 ($\frac{1}{2}$ ton f/in^2). The hand-operated machine is designed so that using the handle provided fully tightening the press attains a similar pressure.

The mould is now left to form completely, i.e. the rubber will now flow around the models into the crevices giving a perfect replicated cavity. The curing time varies, depending upon the volume of rubber and thickness of the disc, an approximate guide being ten minutes to allow the mould to reach temperature and then five minutes for each 3 mm

Fig. VIII:32 *Hydraulic vulcanising press, N. Saunders (Metal Products) Ltd.*

($\frac{1}{8}$ in.) of total mould thickness. After the heating cycle is complete, the heating elements should be switched off and the mould allowed to cool to approximately 70°C (158°F) still under pressure. This is to prevent the possibility of tearing sharp edges, which can happen if the patterns are removed or the mould is disturbed whilst it is still very hot. At the end of the complete cycle time, the frame is removed from the vulcanising press and allowed to cool; further care must be taken here as the assembly is heavy and very hot. The mould should be removed from the frame before it has cooled completely, otherwise it may be difficult to get it out because of contraction and a partial vacuum forming within the frame. Similarly, the mould halves should be separated whilst still warm so that the models or patterns may be easily removed. Before parting the mould halves, it is good practice to cut aligning notches on the outside edges of the mould for ease of alignment when reassembling for production use.

Sprues and vents

As soon as the patterns have been removed, and whilst the mould is still warm, the sprues should be cut in. Opinions vary on the subject of sprues and runners and it is difficult to lay down set parameters. In the USA it is common practice to cut sprues so that a gate feeds from the basin to a secondary circular groove, called a runner wheel, and then individual spokes, or sprue gates, feed the pattern cavities. This practice is in line with the use of preformed standard sprues, moulded in with the pattern. In the UK, however, standard sprues are rarely used and they are cut to suit the shape of the model. The tendency is to keep the sprues relatively small and, if necessary, use two or three small sprues, rather than one large one to each cavity. A large sprue can be difficult to suit the pattern and could leave a large lump in an undesirable position on the casting which has to be cleaned off. It seems preferable to initially cut the sprues small and try a cast and examine the result. The sprue can then be enlarged, or secondary sprues cut to suit. Before enlarging sprues after a trial cast it is essential to thoroughly examine the casting, as the problem may well be resolved by cutting a vent rather than a larger sprue. The points to remember are the functions that the sprues perform:

Fig. VIII:33   *Typical mould, half showing sprueways and locating nuts, Phoenix Model Developments Ltd.*

Fig. VIII:34   *A mould with sprueways and secondary runners to feed multi-cavities, Minutia Models Ltd.*

Fig. VIII:35   *Preparing a mould with cut outs for deep cavities, N. Saunders (Metal Products) Ltd.*

a To deliver enough metal to fill the cavity.

b To fill the cavity quickly to avoid premature freezing or excessive molten metal temperature.

c To allow the metal to flow freely with little turbulence.

Vent cuts are made with a sharp knife, so that the slot is very fine enabling air to pass through but not the higher viscosity metal. Unless experience makes it obvious where vents should be cut, it is preferable to make trial casts and then cut as required. Vent holes can be drilled with fine drills to critical parts of a casting through the back of the mould and runways cut to the periphery of the mould with a sharp knife.

The process of mould-making just described may be classified as squash mould-making, as the patterns, or models, were simply pressed into the two halves of the mould thus forming the cavities. This method is quite suitable and acceptable for small models or shallow cavities or rounded models. However, for more complex shapes with undercuts, or irregular forms or deep sections, it may be necessary to actually cut out the cavities by hand. This also can apply to models where the parting line could significantly affect the appearance of the finished casting. If part of a model is relatively deep and hollow, then the rubber that is cut out of one half may need to be stuck back on the other half in the corresponding position. If cavities need to be preformed, they should be cut out to suit the model as closely as possible. Difficult areas, such as undercuts or gaps, can be filled in with small pieces of rubber as close as possible. These will flow and amalgamate, during the vulcanising process, to form the desired shape.

It is also possible to use inserts, either permanent or temporary, with rubber moulds. For example, a hinge plate can be cast with a pin positioned in the mould prior to casting, so that on completion the pin can be pulled out of the casting, leaving a corresponding hole. Alternatively, fixing pins or screw inserts can be positioned in the mould prior to casting so that the molten metal flows around them and they become part of the casting. For some complex shapes, particularly sculptured pieces such as a winged bird or a figure with an arm or leg not in the same plane as the body, it is possible to use a removable insert block which fits in the rubber mould. Such a block can be made from the same material as the main mould. A small mould frame is used to make a two-part mould of part of the figure, say the wing or the leg. This mould is cured and cooled and smoothed off on the outside. It is then attached to the pattern figure and placed in the

main mould which has a cavity cut to suit the secondary mould. The figure, with its secondary mould, is coated with graphite and is then moulded into the two halves of the main circular mould. After casting the figure with the secondary mould attached is removed from the main mould as a complete unit.

In centrifugal casting where heavy solid castings are involved it is necessary sometimes to distort the master to counteract the distortion that can occur in the casting due to centrifugal force.

There are also occasions when the use of 'chill blocks' are required adjacent to certain parts of a casting to even out cooling stresses.

Casting

The centrifugal casting machine is specifically designed for the purpose, with the necessary safeguards being part of the basic design. The machine consists of a turntable mounted on a vertical shaft, driven by an electric motor. The turntable is of heavy construction and machined flat and concentric with the shaft. Three sets of columns are attached to the turntable and between each pair of columns is pivoted a weighted arm. The weights on these arms are adjustable, so that the pressure on the mould is variable. A removable top plate completes the assembly. The machine rotates at a variable speed range of 500 to 1,000 rpm, the speed being adjustable by the operator to suit the casting. A typical speed for casting small figures is 650 rpm. The whole is encased by a steel cabinet with a lid. In the lid a chromium-plated steel funnel corresponds with the centre hole in the mould. The machine cannot run unless the lid is closed. Alongside the machine is the metal melting pot which forms an integral part of the system.

The two halves of the rubber mould are dusted with talc such that the two major surfaces and the cavities are coated. The excess powder is shaken off and the mould assembled. The mould is placed on the turntable and the top plate is placed in position. The machine lid is closed and the motor started. As the turntable rotates, the pivoted arms swing up and outwards their inner ends thus applying a downwards force on the top plate, clamping the mould halves tightly together. Once up to the set speed the machine is ready to receive the molten pewter.

The pewter is melted in the adjacent gas-fired pot and held at a typical temperature of 290°C (554°F). The temperature can be varied to suit the particular alloy being used and the items being cast. However, it should not exceed 300°C (572°F) if possible, as the life of the rubber moulds will be shortened. An ideal pewter alloy for this method of

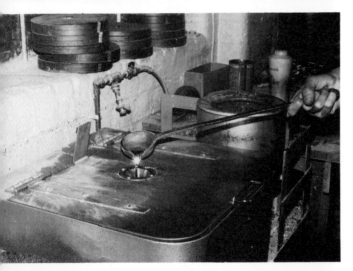

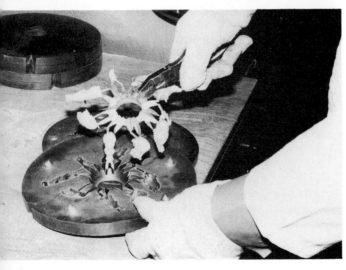

casting is 92% tin, 7.5% antimony, 0.5% copper (Fry's Tandem J 30) as this has a reasonable pasty phase between liquid and solid and therefore gives an ample time period for the casting to form before setting takes place. Care should be taken to see that the metal is ladled out free from dross, as with this method of casting there is little opportunity for the dross to rise to surface of the feeder and there is the possibility of dross being thrown through into the cavities. The ladle should be of such a size, or so marked, that it holds sufficient metal to just fill the cavities, the sprues and the sprue basin. The mould takes a little time to come up to temperature and two or three casts will need to be made before the mould is casting perfectly. Tests have indicated that the rubber mould appears to give its best result when it is at about 100°C (212°F). It is obviously difficult to measure this but experience shows that after three or four consecutive moulds, the castings are at their best. If the mould gets too hot, its life is shortened, so it is good practice to use two or three moulds at a time and cycle them so that each mould has time to cool off slightly. The molten metal should be poured carefully down the centre of the funnel to reduce heat loss into the metal of the funnel. The casting operation is complete within approximately 30 seconds, but it is normal practice to let the machine run for 1 or 2 minutes longer to allow complete solidification and some cooling to take place. Upon completion of the casting cycle the machine is stopped, the lid lifted and the mould removed. The mould halves are separated and the casting allowed to cool a little more. If successive moulds are being used, the next mould can be put in the machine and casting carried out. Whilst this cycle is continuing, the castings can be removed from the first mould. The whole cast assembly comes out in one piece and the individual models are cut away from the sprue gates with strong wire cutters.

The sprues are normally returned to the melting pot. However, the mix in the melting pot should not be allowed to exceed 50% returned metal against 50% virgin metal if the casting is to be of the

Fig. VIII:36 *Centrifugal casting machine, showing turntable, and weighted arms, Phoenix Model Developments Ltd.*

Fig. VIII:37 *Pouring the metal, Phoenix Model Developments Ltd.*

Fig. VIII:38 *Removing the casting from the mould, Phoenix Model Developments Ltd.*

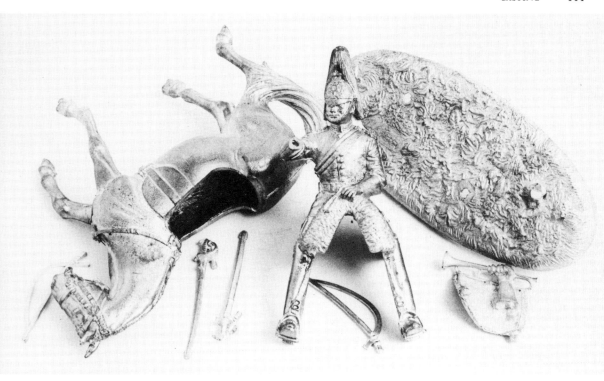

Fig. VIII:39 *Cast parts of a sculptured design, prior to assembly, Buckingham Pewter.*

Fig. VIII:40 *A highly detailed cast sculpture, Buckingham Pewter.*

Fig. VIII:41 *Showing the detail possible in centrifugally cast sculptured pieces, Minutia Models Ltd.*

highest quality. In fact, for castings with large smooth polished areas it is advisable to use 100% virgin material. Experiences will show which type and style of casting can cope with reworked material.

The final castings can then be finished as required by the design by further handwork with file and or wire brush, machine-polishing or tumbling.

Mould life is dependent upon a number of factors and varies from hundreds of casts to thousands. Patterns or moulds with very deep undercuts or sharp edges will give a relatively short life, as thin sections of rubber will eventually break away and detail will be lost. It is essential, therefore, that this type of mould be examined for deterioration after every few casts. Small rounded patterns will give a life of two to three thousand before any substantial deterioration occurs.

The use of centrifugal rubber moulding process has given the designer and caster much more scope in reproducing beautiful and extremely detailed sculptures. The flexibility of the rubber mould, its ability to faithfully accept the detail form and the

Fig. VIII:42 *A finely detailed centrifugal cast sculpture. Buckingham Pewter. (opposite)*

Fig. VIII:43 *A selection of waxes for modelling, Leybourn Needham Ltd. (above)*

casting pressure applied by the centrifugal force now make possible the mass production of articles that previously could only be produced on a one-off basis.

LOST WAX CASTING

Lost wax or investment casting is one of the oldest methods of casting. It consists of forming a mould, using a special plaster, around a wax model and then melting out the wax leaving an impression to be filled with metal. The plaster can withstand very high temperatures and this method of casting is in common use in the jewellery industry for silver and gold. Its use in the pewter industry has declined since the introduction of silicone rubber moulds which can withstand molten pewter temperatures.

There is however still a use for the technique in specific areas and instances. Complex, one-piece art

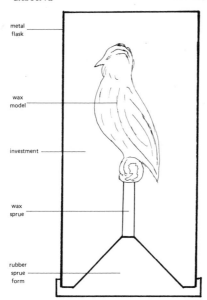

Fig. VIII:44   *Wax model attached to rubber sprue base, J. A. Murrell.*

Diag. VIII:4   *Showing fundamentals of lost-wax casting.*

castings with very deep undercuts can be produced by the lost wax process, whereas with silicone rubber the undercuts would need to be less severe and the casting would probably have to be made in a number of pieces. The significant difference being that in the lost wax process the mould is broken away from the finished casting.

The system is eminently suitable for one-off castings or very large castings where silicone rubber would be expensive. It must be borne in mind of course, that both the model and the mould are destroyed. Whilst it it possible to create quantities of wax models from silicone rubber moulds made from a master, there seems little point in this exercise with regard to pewter which can be cast directly into the rubber moulds.

As the system is in common use there is a range of equipment and materials commercially available.

Master model

The master model is produced as discussed previously (pp. 100–101) though in this case it must be made from wax. There are a number of different waxes available, but they must be classified as investment waxes to be of any use, as it is essential that they burn out from the mould without leaving any residue. These specifically formulated waxes work well with simple tools warmed in a bunsen burner flame or methylated spirit flame and finished to a high gloss.

Mould preparation – small castings

The mould is made in a flask, which is basically a short length of stainless steel tube to withstand the high temperature. These flasks are available commercially in a range of diameters and lengths. To go with the range of flasks, conical rubber bases called sprue bases are also available. The flask chosen should be of a diameter which allows at least 15 mm ($\frac{5}{8}$ in.) clearance all around the model. The length of the flask must be at least 15 mm ($\frac{5}{8}$ in.) longer than the model plus the sprue gate plus the height of the rubber sprue base.

The model should be attached to the rubber sprue base by a sprue or sprues made from wax rod of circular section. Experience will eventually determine the best way and sizes of sprueing.

The sprue should be attached to the heaviest part of the model but away from decorative areas or obvious points as finally it has to be sawn off and the area filed up. The opposite end of the sprue is attached to the sprue base. The wax sprue can be stuck to the wax model and the base by heating the corresponding surfaces or by using a molten sticky wax. The length of the sprue depends on the overall model, but a length of 10–12 mm ($\frac{3}{8}$–$\frac{1}{2}$ in.) is reasonable.

It is advisable at this stage to rinse the wax model in a proprietary wetting agent or a very mild detergent mixture. This cleans the wax and prevents the formation of minute air bubbles at the surface.

Investment

Only special formulated investment powder must be used, as ordinary plaster or plaster of Paris is unsuitable for the high temperatures involved. It is essential to work to the manufacturer's instructions in proportions and mixing. Care should be taken in mixing to avoid beating in air. The powder is added to the water and mixed for approximately 3–4 minutes until it is smooth. Use a small brush to paint the model with this mixture making sure that it is well in details, undercuts and crevices. Fit the flask onto the rubber sprue base and gently pour in the investment down one side of the flask allowing it to flood up over the model until the flask is full. It is essential now to remove the air, and this can be done by tapping the sides of the flask. If a vacuum pot is available, then the investment flask is placed inside the pot and the vacuum applied for 3–4 minutes. A paper collar some 50 cm (2 in.) high should be fitted to the top of the flask as the investment will bubble up initially as the air escapes. Once the air has been removed, the flask should be allowed to stand for approximately 45 minutes to allow the investment to harden off.

Burn out and firing

This is the stage where the wax is melted out from the mould. The rubber sprue base is removed from the flask and the flask is positioned upside down on a wire grill. The wax can be melted out either in an oven set to approximately 150°C (302°F) or by sitting the wire grill and flask over a gas ring set at a medium setting. Once all the wax has run out, or been burnt away in the case of the gas ring, the flask is ready for firing. Care should be taken to ensure adequate ventilation.

Firing can only be carried out really satisfactorily in a specially designed kiln. There are many avail-

Fig. VIII:45 *Vacuum pump, tank, casting table and flasks. (Photo: V. N. Barrett & Co. Ltd)*

Fig. VII:46   *The finished casting with flask and plaster broken away, J. A. Murrell. (left)*

Fig. VIII:47   *A homemade steam caster, based on the solbrig system, J. A. Murrell. (right)*

Fig. VIII:48   *A complete beginners outfit for lost-wax casting. (Photo: V. N. Barrett & Co. Ltd)*

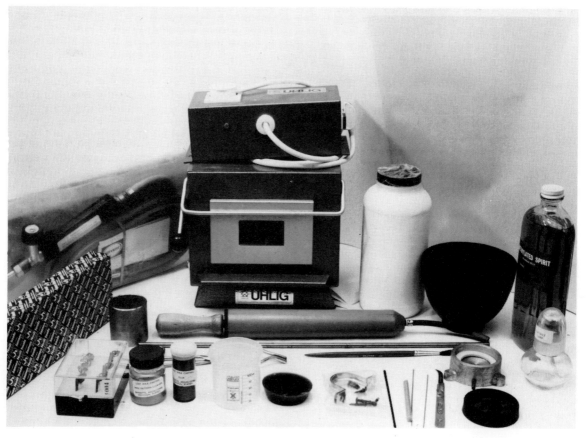

able commercially, both gas and electrically heated. The flask, still hot direct from the burn out phase, is placed in the kiln which is then switched on and set to its highest setting, approximately 900°C (1650°F). After an hour, depending upon the size of the flask, the whole flask and mould will appear white hot. Turn the kiln setting down to approximately 500°C (932°F) and leave for a further 30–40 minutes.

Mould preparation – large castings

For large castings the process is similar except that the flask is usually a large box. Alternatively, the wax mould can be coated with several layers of investment slurry until a thick coating is obtained. The box mould is made suitable for gravity casting in a manner similar to sand casting by the provision of feeders and runners. Firing of the mould is carried out in a similar manner, though a larger kiln or oven is required, and the process time is longer.

Casting

The large moulds are usually gravity cast in a manner similar to sand casting or metal mould casting. The smaller castings, however, need to be cast by some pressure system, as this type of moulding process does not easily give the opportunity to provide air to escape. The air must be forced out through the porosity of the investment. The pressure systems available are centrifugal, vacuum, air pressure and steam pressure. The most common being centrifugal and vacuum.

Vacuum

A vacuum pot evacuated by a pump or a water venturi is attached by a rubber or plastic pipe to a hollow base plate designed to support the flask. A washer of heat resistant material such as neoprene is fitted into the base plate to form an airtight seal between the flask and the base plate. A tap is fitted to the pipe connecting the base plate to the vacuum chamber.

Whilst the flask is still in the kiln the pewter can be prepared for melting. The flask is removed from the kiln and placed onto the base plate. The molten pewter is ladled from the melting pot and poured into the top of the hot mould. The surface tension of the molten pewter and the small diameter of the sprue may prevent the pewter initially from running into the mould. As soon as the conical sprue feed hold is full the tap is opened and the vacuum chamber draws the air from the mould cavity. The consequent imbalance of pressure causes the molten pewter to be forced into the mould by the atmospheric air pressure.

It is essential that the correct volume of metal is used. Too little, and the casting will be incomplete, too much and molten metal will overflow the mould and spatter. An easy method of finding the correct volume is to immerse completely the pattern including the sprues and sprue base into a container of water and mark the level. Remove the pattern and immerse pieces of pewter until the water returns to the same level.

Once the metal has solidified and cooled, the whole flask can be dropped into a bucket of cold water. This sudden cooling will break up the investment away from the casting. Final cleaning can be carried out with a wire brush and a scriber to clean investment from crevices. The sprues can be cut off with strong wire cutters and cleaned back to the casting with a file.

Centrifugal

Simple machines are available commercially and operate either in a vertical plane or a horizontal plane. The machine consists of two arms mounted on a shaft. On one arm is a support cradle for a crucible and a moulding flask. Initially the two arms are balanced by positioning the flask, crucible and correct volume of metal on one arm and adjusting a counter balance weight on the other. The arms are then wound back against a spring and held by a safety catch. The metal is melted in the crucible using a blow torch. The hot flask is placed in the cradle immediately behind the crucible. A hole in the back of the crucible lining up with the entrance to the sprue in the mould. The metal is reheated and when molten, the torch is removed and the safety catch released. The arms spin round under the tension of the spring and centrifugal force throws the molten metal through the back of the crucible into the mould. Care must be taken to get the torch well clear before releasing the safety catch. For safety the whole machine is surrounded by a metal casing and the arms should be allowed to come to rest of their own accord before removing the flask.

Steam pressure

This system is in common use in the jewellery trade and is known as the Solbrig system after the original designer. A base plate has at one end a column into which is hinged a handle. Halfway along the handle is a cast metal lid which is approximately 25 mm (1 in.) larger in diameter than the particular flask to be used. Inside the lid is a thick soft asbestos washer. The hot flask is placed on the base board immediately below the lid. The metal is poured into the flask or melted *in situ*. The asbestos washer is well damped with water and replaced in the lid. When the metal is ready to cast, the lid is brought down to seal the top of the flask. The heat from the metal and the hot flask causes steam to be generated from the damp asbestos and the pressure from the steam forces the metal into the mould. After approximately 30 seconds the pressure can be released. Care needs to be taken with this process until experience is gained.

Air pressure

This is similar in principle to the steam system. In this case, however, the lid forms the lower part of the air chamber approximately 50 mm (2 in.) in diameter and 30 cm (1 ft) high. The air chamber is pressurised from a foot pump to approximately 138 kN/m² (20 lb f in.²). Once the molten metal is ready to cast, the air chamber is placed firmly over the flask and the air pressure released to the flask. After approximately 30 seconds the air chamber can be removed.

Summary

This form of casting is relatively cheap and gives the opportunity of producing one-piece castings of articles which by other methods would be of necessity two or three parts. It is by its nature a one-off exercise as far as pewter is concerned for although wax copies can be produced in rubber moulds, these same rubber moulds will readily accept molten pewter. The temperatures and other dimensions given in the text are for guidance as the number of variables are such that only by trial and error will the exact conditions be determined.

Safety

As in all forms of casting, care must be taken. Gloves should be worn and a leather apron in case of splatter. Safety goggles are cheap and easily available and should always be worn when pouring molten metal. Flasks ready for casting are very hot and must be handled with suitable crucible tongs.

VULCANISED RUBBER MOULD CASTING

Although the major use of vulcanised rubber in the pewter industry is to produce moulds for use in centrifugal casting machines, it is eminently suitable for single castings. Whilst it will not give the mould life of traditional metal moulds, some of which are over 100 years old and still in use, it is capable of a good economic life in production use. The rubber mould has the great capability of producing quite intricate detailed castings and surface finish, which is not possible with metal moulds without considerable tooling expenditure. Even then, there are limitations with regard to undercuts and crevices which the flexibility of the rubber overcome. The alternative of lost wax casting to produce intricate castings has the disadvantage of being a one-off, where the mould is destroyed each time. A well-designed and formed rubber mould will give many castings and is easily replaced even to the extent of the new mould using one of the castings as its patterns.

Casting techniques with vulcanised rubber moulds are similar to the process described under silicone rubber casting (pp. 100–106).

Moulds

Moulds are produced in a manner similar to that described for centrifugal machine casting using thick sheets of unvulcanised rubber cut and profiled as required. Alternatively, the rubber can be completely moulded around the pattern and then cut open after vulcanising. In either case the mould should be produced in a metal frame.

Complete mould

Place the mould frame, having dusted it with graphite, on a flat surface and line the bottom with a sheet or sheets of unvulcanised rubber. Position the pattern so as to allow room for the sprue gate and press into the layer of rubber. Use pieces of rubber cut to approximately the shape to fill in around the pattern. Lay further sheets on top until the frame is over-full by approximately 10%.

Clamp the whole assembly in a press, having coated the top and bottom plates with graphite, and vulcanise. Large moulds need to be vulcanised in a commercial press as previously described in centrifugal casting (pp. 106–13). For small moulds, a simple hand-press will suffice and the vulcanising carried out in a domestic oven set at 150°C (302°F). Initially, the press should be tightened to just squeeze the rubber, and heated for approximately 15 minutes. The press can now be fully tightened and left in the oven for 1½ to 2 hours. The mould should be allowed to cool until it is comfortable to handle. Push the mould out of the frame and carefully cut through, on a desired parting line, to the pattern. One edge may be left uncut to act as a hinge so that the mould opens like a book. This makes for accurate alignment, but the mould can be cut right through and keys cut in the corners during the process. Sprue gates and vents are now cut in the mould to suit the pattern and the casting technique.

CUTTLEFISH BONE CASTING

Cuttlefish casting is a traditional way of producing simple castings, often in precious metals and is in common use in the jewellery trade. It is ideal for pewter castings as it stands up to the molten temperatures very well. Its use is limited to small patterns of low relief form, such as brooches,

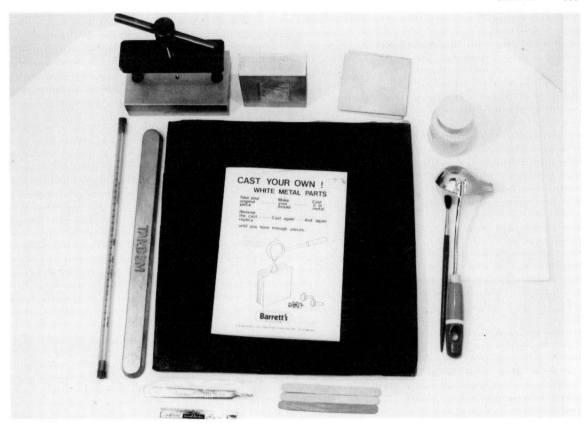

Fig. VIII:49 *A beginners kit for vulcanised rubber moulding and casting. (Photo: V. N. Barrett & Co. Ltd)*

medallions and fobs, or for simple shapes such as rings or pendants, to give the basic shape for later finishing. The pattern must be of a hard material such as metal, hardwood or hard plastic as the mould is formed by pressing the pattern into the surface of the cuttlefish bone. Cuttlefish can be obtained from pet shops, ironmongers or jewellery supply shops. The latter usually stock a superior grade of bone than the pet shops. Pieces of bone come in various sizes and thicknesses and have on one side a hard bony surface, whilst the other side is relatively soft and grainy.

Making the mould

Two pieces of cuttlefish are required, and the soft face of each piece is filed and sanded perfectly flat to give a pair of mating surfaces. The hard pattern is then pressed into the face of one piece by gentle hand pressure, being careful not to snap the bone. The pattern should be pressed in to approximately half its depth. To ease the pressure required, and to prevent snapping the bone, it should be gently scraped away in the deeper areas of the pattern. Only approximate depressions should be scraped away, so that there is no danger of losing the final shape. Three or four locating pins are now placed in

the first half of the cuttlefish in order to align the second half. Matchsticks, rivets or ball bearings can be used as locating pins. Clean any loose dust out of the first half and reinsert the pattern. Line the second half up with the first and square the two halves together. This is best done between the hands as the movements of the two pieces can be felt, and pressure adjusted to suit. The two halves are separated and a sprue feed way cut in with a sharp knife or scalpel. The sprue way should be as large as possible without of course interfering too much with the final casting. If the pattern is irregular, the sprue should be opposite the thickest part. The mould is next examined for possible airlocks, and vents cut with a scalpel or scratched in with a finely pointed scriber or large needle. All traces of dust must be blown out of the mould and the surfaces lightly coated with a very thin oil. This coating helps reduce the pattern of the grain of the cuttlefish and seals the general porosity. The two halves are reassembled, making sure that the locating pins

Fig. VIII:50   *The two halves of the cuttlefish mould with pattern and locating balls, J. A. Murrell.*

Fig. VIII:51   *Pouring into cuttlefish mould, showing also a completed casting, J. A. Murrell.*

register exactly. The two halves can be bound together with soft iron wire or strong adhesive tape such as carpet tape. The completed mould should then be stood in a sand tray or other receptacle to catch any overspill of molten metal.

Casting

For small castings such as this, the pewter can be melted directly in the ladle with a gas torch. As only a small volume of pewter is required, it needs to be heated well above its melting temperature to prevent premature cooling on pouring. Pour the molten metal down one side of the sprue hole in the inclined mould until full. Allow the mould to cool for at least five minutes before opening as cuttlefish is a good insulator. The sprue can then be sawn off and the casting finished as required.

Provided the pattern or design has no really sharp edges, cuttlefish moulds are capable of producing several castings.

SAND CASTING

Casting into sand moulds is an age-old process developed over the centuries. Its use in the pewter industry has declined over the years, but recent developments in the process and techniques could make it once more attractive.

The development of easily used and reusable oil-bound sands, as opposed to water-bound sands, also make the use of sand casting attractive to the pewter industry.

In its basic form, the process is suitable for both the individual pewtersmith and the commercial factory. In this text, therefore, the basic techniques will be described, as even the most sophisticated methods available still start from this basic process.

Patterns

The pattern can be made from wood, plastic, wax, or be an original item if it can be withdrawn from the sand mould. Depending upon its shape and the way that it can be withdrawn from the mould, the pattern can be in one piece or two halves dowelled together. If the item is hollow, then a second pattern box is required to produce a sand core to the shape of the inside of the item to be cast.

When producing a pattern, allowance must be made for any machining that may be desirable. If parts have to finish to a precise dimension then a shrinkage allowance must be made, though in pewterware this is probably unnecessary. To facilitate withdrawal from the mould the pattern must be designed so that it tapers towards the lower end or bottom of the mould. Square sides must be given a draw angle of approximately 2 mm in 30 cm ($\frac{1}{4}$ in. in 1 foot) to avoid breaking away the sand when the pattern is withdrawn. Wooden patterns should be made from a close-grained wood, easy to carve.

For intricate carving and detail, it is possible to obtain sheets of self-adhesive wax. The sheet wax can be cut to shape and stuck and smoothed on to a wooden pattern so that it gives the appearance of a wax model. Surface detail and design can then be cut and formed using wax modelling tools. Finished wooden patterns and core boxes should be given one or two coats of polyurethane gloss varnish.

Moulding

Solid pattern

The first example is a simple solid, flat-based pattern. Two boxes are required to contain the sand. These boxes can be made from wood or be proprietary metal moulding boxes. The two boxes must fit together accurately, one on top of the other, and be located by pegs or lugs with some means of locking them together. A strong flat board called a moulding board is also required.

The lower box, called the drag, is placed on the moulding board and the pattern positioned centrally. The pattern is now covered with an oil-bound

Fig. VIII:52 *Metal moulding box, consisting of drag and cope located and locked together, Les Potstainiers Hutois.*

Fig. VIII:53 *Removing patterns from moulding box, Les Potstainiers Hutois.*

moulding sand such as Lutron. This is an excellent sand for pewter or other nonferrous metals as it is very free-flowing, very fine to give excellent detail and surface finish and compacts easily without excessive ramming. Initially, sufficient sand to cover just the pattern is poured in and pressed well into the shape using hands and fingers. When this is

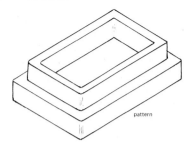

pattern

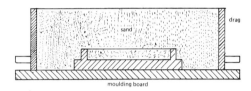

Diag. VIII:5 *Showing drag or bottom moulding box rammed up.*

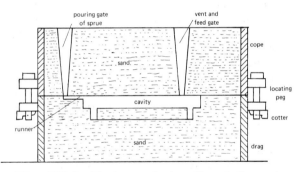

Diag. VIII:6 *Showing completed mould, ready for pouring.*

complete, the box is filled with sand which is rammed down with shaped wooden rammers working in from the edges of the box. Further sand is rammed in until the box is slightly over-full, then using a metal straight edge the sand is levelled off with the edges of the box.

Holding the moulding board in position the lower box or drag is completely turned over. The upper box, called the cope, is then placed on top, located and locked into position. A thin film of parting agent is now sprinkled over the surface of the rammed sand and pattern in the drag. This is to prevent the sand in the top box adhering to the sand in the bottom box and making it impossible to part them. Suitable agents are very dry sharp sand, brick

dust, coal dust or graphite or mixtures of these. At this stage a preformed sprue gate or pouring gate may be placed in position, or alternatively a sprue way may be cut in after ramming, using a metal tube with a sharpened edge. In either case, the sprue gate should not pass directly into the mould cavity but should feed via a runner so that metal flows into the mould in a gentle manner without damage to the mould cavity. The cope is now filled with sand and rammed as before and levelled off with the straight edge. Either a single vent hole can be cut into the cope box using a sharpened metal tube or alternatively two or three smaller vents can be produced by pushing a thin wire through the sand until it touches the pattern and then being withdrawn. The cope is unlocked and removed from the drag, care being taken not to disturb the sand. The pattern can now be removed from the drag, and this is best done by screwing into the pattern a large wood screw or threaded metal rod. The rod, known as a draw spike, is tapped gently in all directions, which has the effect of slightly enlarging the mould cavity, making it possible to withdraw the pattern without disturbing the sand. Using a knife or a piece of shaped metal, a runner slot is cut in the sand from the sprue gate to the mould cavity. The two halves of the mould should then be examined for any loose particles which should be blown away. The cope is then refitted to the drag and locked in position ready for pouring.

Split pattern

Patterns for items without one flat side are usually better made in two halves fitted together with dowel pins. The two pieces do not necessarily have to be exact halves as the design itself can determine the best joint line. However, it must be borne in mind that each half must be of such a shape that it can be removed from the sand mould. The procedure for making the mould is similar to that of a one-piece pattern. The half containing the dowel holes is placed on the moulding board in the bottom box and rammed up as before. After reversing the drag, the second half of the pattern is fitted to the half already in the sand, alignment being by the dowels. The cope is positioned and the procedure for ramming and gating carried out as previously described (pp. 121–2).

Cored pattern

Hollow items require sand core and the pattern requires extensions known as core prints to allow positioning of the core in the mould. The basic pattern can be either solid or split, depending upon the design of the required item.

In order to produce the core, a split mould must

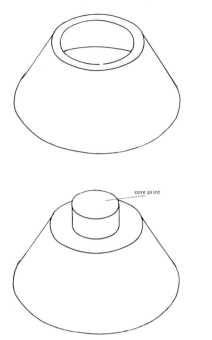

Diag. VIII:7 *Showing solid pattern to produce the hollow casting.*

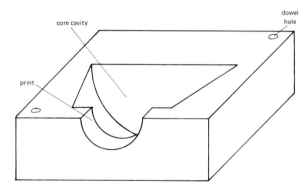

Diag. VIII:8 *Showing construction of core box.*

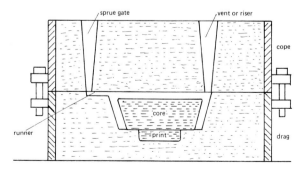

Diag. VIII:9 *Showing cored mould ready for pouring.*

be made, machined or carved to the internal shape required. In addition to the basic shape one or two extensions must be machined in for the core to sit in the core print in the mould. To produce the core, special core sands are available containing resins, which, with the addition of a catalyst, will air harden or bake into a readily handled core. These core sands are designed so that they will withstand reasonable handling and the effect of molten metal being poured over them, yet break away quite easily from the inside of the finished casting. The core sand should be mixed as per the manufacturer's instruction and moulded in the core box. Setting times are relatively short, after which the core mould is opened and the core allowed to air dry or be baked in an oven as required.

The basic pattern is as before, to the exact external shape of the required item, but with the addition of extensions, to suit the core design, known as core prints. The sand mould is made in the drag and the cope as previously explained. This time, however, after the pattern is removed, the core is placed in position resting in the core prints before the drag and the cope are reassembled. The mould is then ready to receive the molten metal. After casting and removal from the mould, the core can be broken out from the hollow casting with a spiked tool or an old screwdriver, care being taken not to damage the casting.

Casting

The oil-bound sand suggested for use in pewter casting has very good insulating properties and molten metal flows well over its surface. Consequently, there is no need for excessive temperatures in the molten metal and pewter can be poured at around 300°C (572°F). Furthermore, as there is no moisture in the sand, as in the previous water-sand mixtures, there is no danger of spluttering or steam cavitation on the surfaces.

Like all casting procedures, only experience determines the ideal position for sprue gates, feeders and vents. It may be found advantageous to increase the height of the sprue gate by the addition of a sand collar and thus increase the head pressure for improved mould filling. Depending upon the shape and size of the casting it may be found that improvements to the casting can be made by using one large vent or riser similar in size to the sprue or pouring gate. This has the effect of easy venting and also acting as a secondary feeder of molten metal as the main casting cools and draws from it, thus reducing cooling stress marks. However, large sprues and vents give more work in the fettling process.

As the sand is such a good insulator ample time

Fig. VIII:54   *Showing moulding box, split pattern, core and core box, and finished castings with sprue and riser, Les Potstainiers Hutois.*

Diag. VIII:10   *Showing a split pattern for a hollow casting.*

Diag. VIII:11   *Showing lower moulding box rammed up.*

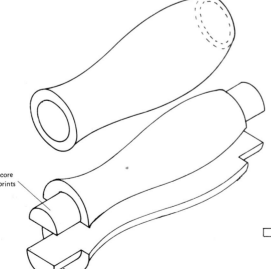

core prints

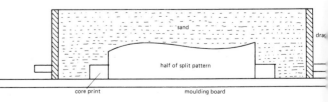

sand

drag

half of split pattern

core print   moulding board

must be allowed for the metal to solidify before the mould is broken open. The sand is reusable many times, provided it is not contaminated, so care should be taken to break open the mould over some form of container, so as to save the sand for reuse. After a time the binder in the sand may need replenishing, as a little burns out at each casting, but this is only a small proportion of the total volume and mixes in readily.

Castings produced by this method should require the minimum of machining and in many cases can be linished or polished direct from casting.

PLASTER CASTINGS

A number of special foundry plasters are available for making moulds for metal casting for tem-

Fig. VIII:55 *Some examples of sand-cast pewter, Les Potstainiers Hutois.*

Diag. VIII:12 *Showing complete mould for hollow item ready for pouring.*

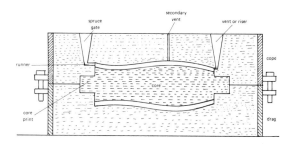

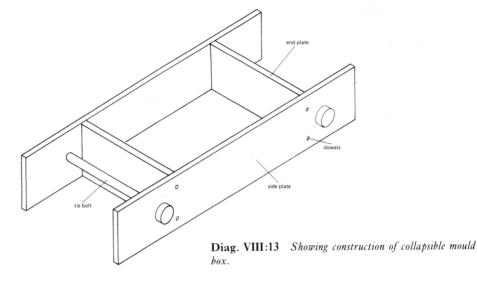

Diag. VIII:13 *Showing construction of collapsible mould box.*

peratures not greater than 900°C (1,560°F). This makes them ideal for pewter casting, with its molten temperature well within the required range. A plaster such as Herculite is specially formulated to give excellent surface finish, easy mixing and crack-free drying.

Patterns

Patterns can be of any material, but must be of good finish and free from any superfluous marks, as these will be reproduced in the finished casting.

Wooden patterns should be treated with varnish or cellulose pattern enamel and polished with wax. Plaster patterns can be used, but must be coated with two or three layers of parting medium applied with cotton wool, making sure that it penetrates into intricate parts. A suitable parting medium is one part stearic acid to three parts paraffin, or alternatively petroleum jelly may be used in place of stearic acid.

Moulding boxes

Moulding boxes can be made of wood or metal. If made of wood, then they should be painted with cellulose pattern enamel to avoid the take-up of water from the plaster.

In order to facilitate easy removal of the plaster mould prior to final drying, collapsible boxes are to be preferred. The boxes should consist of two side plates and two end plates with all edges machined flat and square. The side plates extend beyond the end plates so that tie bolts can pass across, thus clamping the assembly together. Dowel pins should be fitted into the ends of the end plates with corresponding holes in the side plates.

Top and bottom plates should be available similar to the cope and drag boxes used in sand castings (pp. 121–3), with a means of locating and locking them together. It is possible with plaster casting to use only one deep box and its method of use will be explained later (pp. 127–8). A moulding board is also required, but this must be absolutely flat so a machined metal plate is preferable to wood.

Mixing the plaster

Herculite foundry plaster should be mixed in the proportion of 100 parts plaster to 110 parts water by weight, 0.91 kg of plaster to 1 litre of water (1.14 lb/ 1 pint). The plaster should be sprinkled into the water and allowed to soak for a minute or two before stirring. The stirring should be slow and gentle to avoid entrapping air, but must be thorough so that the mixture is smooth and creamy without lumps.

Mould making

The process is similar to that described in the section on sand casting (pp. 121–3), with regard to the various types of patterns and cores. In the case of plaster casting, the cores would be made of plaster, moulded in a core box similar to that used for making sand cores.

The pattern is positioned on the mould board and the moulding box assembled around it so that the pattern is in the centre. The pattern, the mould board and the inside of the moulding box are painted with the parting medium previously described.

The liquid plaster is poured slowly into one corner of the box so that it flows across the pattern surface, thus displacing the air immediately in contact with the pattern. Once the pattern is com-

pletely covered, the plaster can be gently agitated with the fingers or a brush immersed below the surface to dispel any air bubbles adjacent to the pattern. Pouring should then continue until the mould is full. If the pattern is very light it may be found that it tends to float in the plaster. To prevent this a weighted steel pin can be stuck into the back of the pattern to hold it down.

The plaster will set off in approximately 25 minutes and at this stage the box can be lifted off the moulding board and inverted. It is desirable at this stage to ease the pattern free from the mould by removing the holding down pin and applying compressed air or by gently tapping the pin. The pattern should then be replaced in the mould and the surface coated with parting medium.

The top moulding box and the second half of the pattern are then placed in position. At this stage, a preformed ingate may also be positioned. After coating all surfaces with parting medium, the remainder of the plaster is poured, to fill the top box, taking precautions as before to avoid air bubbles.

Once the plaster is set off the two moulding boxes can be parted and the pattern removed. Runners should be cut in at this stage, before the final hardening of the plaster, for it cuts cleanly in its green state. If no ingate was performed, it can be cut in with a tube cutter or even drilled using a hand drill and metal cutting drill. The ingates can be of relatively small diameter as the insulating properties of the plaster are very high and therefore the rate of cooling of the molten metal is slow. Vents can be drilled in a similar manner or holes

Fig. VIII:56 *Pouring the plaster, Moruplast Ltd.*

Fig. VIII:57 *A single deep moulding box with a shaped moulding board, Moruplast Ltd.*

pierced with a wire. Alternatively, vent cuts can be made on one of the surfaces to the outside edge of the mould.

The plaster moulds are then ready for final drying and can be dried in the mould box or the mould box can be disassembled.

The moulds are best left for a further two hours in ambient conditions before being placed in a drying oven. If possible, the oven should be of the forced air circulation type and thermostatically controlled. The oven should be set to reach no more than 195°C (383°F) and the drying time allowed should be 24 hours for moulds of 75–100 mm (3–4 in.) thickness.

Moulds can be produced in a single deep box instead of two separate boxes. With this system there are no alignment problems and it is more convenient, especially with small moulds. The additional requirement when using a single deep box is a moulding board made of wood or metal which is a close fit inside the box and of a thickness equal to half the depth of the box. In use the box is built around the thick moulding board, the pattern or half pattern is placed upon the board and moulding carried out as previously explained (pp. 126–7). When the first half of the plaster mould is set, the box is slackened off and the moulding board is removed. The first half of the plaster mould now becomes the lower half, the box is built around it,

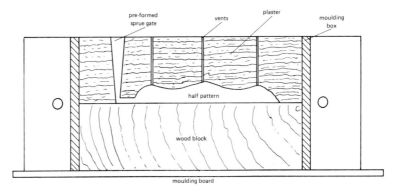

the pattern positioned and moulding completed. It is essential to remember to coat all of the inside surfaces of the box, the outside of the pattern and the surface of the lower mould with parting medium, prior to pouring the plaster for the top half of the mould.

Small moulds can be made without using boxes by the use of right-angled metal strips sealed with plasticine exactly as explained in the section on silicone rubber moulding (pp. 101–3).

Casting

Casting can be carried out by gravity or pressure methods, as the plaster sets very hard and is capable of withstanding pressures similar to low pressure die casting.

Excessive melt temperatures are not required as the insulating properties of the plaster are very high. This must be borne in mind after casting and sufficient time allowed for the metal to solidify before breaking open the mould. Experience will eventually determine the setting time for a given mould, but as a rough guide, on a weight for weight basis, the following may help. Compared with a metal mould setting time, allow five times for a sand mould and ten times for a plaster mould.

Gravity

For gravity casting, the runners and vents should be as for gravity sand castings. It is preferable to use the plaster moulds whilst they are still warm and dry from the oven. If it is not possible to use them immediately, then they must be stored in a warm dry atmosphere to avoid any absorption of moisture.

In order to give a good head pressure to the casting, it is advantageous to position a feed tube 100–150 mm (4–6 in.) in height above the ingate. This should be a metal tube with a plaster lining which can be moulded and dried along with the main mould.

The molten pewter which need only be at 260°C (470°F) should be ladled from the melting pot, after skimming the dross from the surface, and poured

Diag. VIII:14 *Showing method of producing half a mould in a complete box.*

gently into the mould until the ingate is full.

Once the casting is solid, the mould can be broken open and the plaster knocked off. Any plaster adhering to the casting can be brushed off in water once the casting is cold.

Pressure

Air pressure can be used as a means of providing pressure for casting in plaster moulds. In order to do this, some additional equipment is required as well as a source of compressed air at 34–69 kN/m² (5–10 lb f in²). The equipment consists of a top plate that can be clamped to the top of the mould box plus a tubular reservoir that can be clamped to the top plate. The tubular reservoir, in turn, has a cover which can be clamped in place and in the cover is a connection to a compressed air line. The reservoir, which is lined with plaster, aligns with a hole in the top plate which in turn aligns with the ingate hole in the mould. A bursting disc of heat-resistant material is also required which clamps between the reservoir and the top plate.

In use, after the parts have been assembled, molten metal is poured into the reservoir, which is of such a size as to contain sufficient volume of metal for the casting and the ingate. The cover is closed and clamped on the reservoir and the air valve opened to allow compressed air into the reservoir. Provided the bursting disc is of the correct thickness, it will rupture and allow the molten metal to flow into the mould under pressure. Alternatively, the disc can be ruptured with a spike just prior to the lid being closed and the air pressure being applied. In this system, vents should be cut very fine so as to only allow the escape of air.

After a short while, the air pressure can be released and the reservoir removed for use on another mould whilst the original casting is allowed to set and cool. In removing the reservoir it may be found that the lower part of the lining breaks away. It is common practice to make the lining in two parts, an upper and lower, and to renew the lower part for each cast.

Reusable moulds

For short runs and fairly simple objects, plaster moulds are substantial enough for a number of casts.

The ingate, or sprue, must of course be designed into the mould along the split line so that it is possible to open the mould and allow the casting to fall out. The material is ideal for making moulds for slush casting when the cost of metal moulds is prohibitive or the required volume is very low.

The method of manufacture of the mould is basically similar to that described in the section on silicone rubber moulding (see pp. 101–3). The mould can be hand-held with a protective glove, though more time must be allowed than with a metal mould before pouring the metal out again.

PRESSURE DIE CASTING

There are two methods of die casting, high pressure and low pressure. High pressure die casting is mainly for very high volume output and has, of necessity, very high tooling costs. Low pressure die casting is a more suitable process for the sort of volumes expected in the pewter industry. The tool costs are not excessive, as many tools can be cast from aluminium.

The process consists basically of a crucible of molten metal inside a sealed pressure vessel. The lid or cover of the pressure vessel has a tube through it, the lower part extending down into the molten metal and the upper part in contact with the ingate of the die. The die being mounted above the cover and

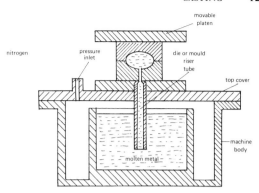

Diag. VIII:16 *Showing the principle of an air-pressure die-casting machine.*

clamped tightly to it, compressed nitrogen at a pressure ranging from 20–30 kN/m^2 (3–5 lb f in^2) is admitted into the pressure vessel, which, acting upon the top surface of the molten metal, forces metal to flow up the tube into the die or mould. Suitable venting is required in the mould to allow for the escape of air as the metal enters. Vents can be similar to those described in rubber moulding (pp. 104–5), that is very fine cuts taken from critical areas to the outside edge of the mould or die. The fine cuts will allow air to escape, but will not leak metal because of its viscosity and solidification rate.

In order to ensure complete filling of die or mould it is sometimes found necessary to provide overflow wells in the mould. These overflow wells are fed by small gates from inconspicuous places in the main casting and often designed so that ejector pins can operate in these areas to push the solidified casting from the mould without damage to the main casting. The solidified overflow wells and the ingate are cut off once the casting is removed from the mould.

The process is relatively gentle and the metal flows into the mould without turbulence and without the danger of entrapping air. Only one ingate is required and, provided the vents are kept small and in inconspicuous places, very little finishing is required. Surface finish can be excellent, particularly if smooth matt metal moulds are used and for most pewter articles only final polishing is required. As the metal is pressure fed in a gentle manner, relatively thin-walled articles can be produced giving strong high-quality castware of relatively low weight.

The fact that only one ingate is required permits greater scope for tool design and the process is ideal for producing large surface area products such as plates and trays.

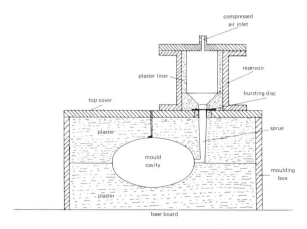

Diag. VIII:15 *Showing the elements of air-pressure casting with plaster mould.*

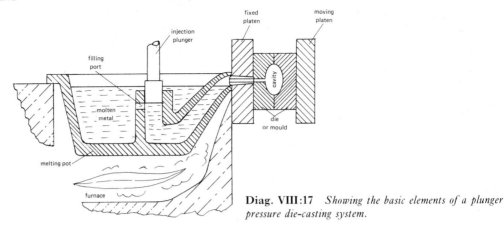

Diag. VIII:17 *Showing the basic elements of a plunger pressure die-casting system.*

Hollow articles can be produced by the use of collapsible cores and it is relatively easy to mould in inserts for attachments of handles or bases.

A number of die casting machines are available, both air pressure and plunger operated, and there is considerable expertise available for mould design.

PERMANENT METAL MOULDS

The manufacture of large and multi-part metal moulds as described in the section on metal mould casting (pp. 91–8) is normally outside the scope of the pewtersmith and the pewter workshop.

It is possible, however, for simple metal moulds, especially those used for slush casting, to be manufactured in the pewter workshop using standard equipment and the technique of sand and/or plaster casting.

The metal used for the moulds can be aluminium or aluminium alloy, pewter or Kirksite which is a zinc alloy. All of these are within the range of the melting pots or torches to be found in the pewter workshop.

Pattern

The pattern can be an original item or a model made from wood, wax or plastic. If made from wood, the pattern should be painted with varnish and wax polished. If an original item is used, it is an advantage to also wax polish this before use, as it makes for an improved mould surface.

Mould manufacture

If the model or pattern is made from any material that melts at a lower temperature than the metal to be used for the final mould, then interstage patterns must be produced.

An ideal medium for this is the plaster discussed in the section on plaster casting (pp. 125–9).

First stage

Following the procedures outlined in the previous sections the pattern or model should be embedded to half its depth in a layer of plasticine. Making due allowances for sprues and vents a box made up from strips of steel should be built around this base. Using the techniques previously explained a plaster cast should be made from the original pattern. This will be a 'negative' pattern.

Second stage

Using the same metal box the 'negative' pattern is placed in the bottom. All of the exposed surfaces must be coated with parting medium and then the plaster poured in. When set this is now a 'positive' pattern or a complete replica of the original.

Third stage

The replica plaster cast now becomes the pattern for the final metal mould. Again using the same metal box the plaster pattern is set in the bottom half. The metal for the final mould is melted and poured in. When cool, it can be removed and one half of the final metal mould is complete.

Second half

The surface of the first or bottom half of the metal mould should be smoothed off and polished, removing as little metal as possible.

The original pattern is positioned in the metal mould and the assembly placed back in the metal frame. A plaster cast is made as before and the steps repeated to produce the second or top half of the metal mould.

The two halves can then be assembled around the original pattern for alignment and holes drilled through for dowel pins.

FAULTS AND PROBLEMS

A number of faults can occur with castings. Many of these are common to all of the methods, whilst some are specific.

Some common faults and the possible reasons or

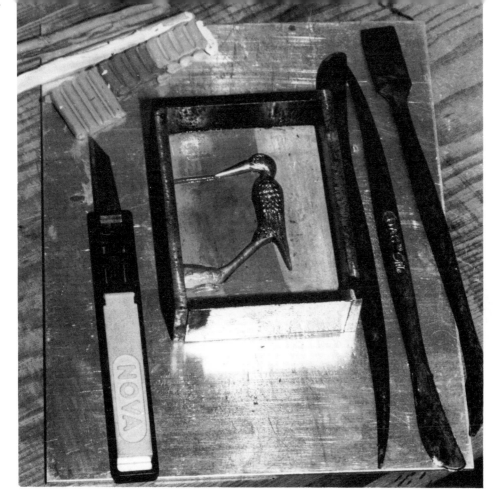

Fig. VIII:58   *The pattern on a plasticine base in a moulding box, ready for first cast, J. A. Murrell.*

areas for investigation are discussed below.

In casting pewter the aim in general terms should be to fill the mould as quickly as possible, have the pewter solidify as quickly as possible and pour the metal at the lowest temperature necessary to fill the mould to achieve a consistently good finish through the casting. As in all things, some compromise and experiment will be needed to attain the best results.

There are two infinitely variable and interrelated components to this requirement – the casting temperature of the metal and the temperature of the mould immediately prior to pouring. Unfortunately, these two factors do not work out in an arithmetical progression, for instance there will be different results from a cast with the metal temperature at 300°C and the mould at 200°C, than from a cast at 350°C and 150°C respectively. Many other factors also have to be considered, e.g. material of the mould and its heat-transfer characteristics, the sections of the moulding itself and the variety of different sections and where they occur in the piece, the arrangement of the vents on the mould, and the size and height of the infeed; it is largely by trial and error and accumulated experience that the most suit-

able compromise will be arrived at. In mould materials, for instance, the results from bronze, which has an excellent heat-transfer characteristic, will be quite different from those of silicone rubber at the other end of the scale, which has a poor heat transfer. The points already made on mould design apply whatever material is used to make the mould but these other factors should also be borne in mind when trying to analyse a faulty casting. It may, for instance, be necessary to make the wall of a silicone rubber mould thin in certain areas to help cooling. Pewter is a sensitive material and shrinks noticeably in cooling, which can leave a 'grainy' or porous surface. It is desirable therefore to try to make the infeed the last place to freeze.

It is often difficult to understand the true reason for a fault in a casting, but the following notes may provide some pointers.

Porosity

Shrinkage due to uneven or incorrect cooling in the mould is the most likely reason. This can well be

caused by changes of section in the casting which it is desirable to avoid if possible. If not, it may be necessary to modify the mould to include 'chills'. Basically freezing in the mould should progress from the outer limits of the casting back towards the ingate so that any shrinkage taking place on cooling will be taken up by metal that is still molten within the mould. If there is an 'island' of molten metal within a mould, porosity will occur when it freezes and contracts.

Cavity not filling/voids, blowholes

If the metal is too cold it will have a shiny finish and the edges of the casting will not be sharp.

If, however, the cast has a matt finish and the vents have filled with pewter it is likely the cavity in the moulding is caused by trapped air. If possible, the mould should be rotated through about 60° when pouring to try to eliminate this pocket, but if this is not successful a vent should be cut or drilled (not more than $\frac{1}{32}$ in.) to allow the trapped air to escape.

Discolouration

It is sometimes said that castings having a gilded finish have been cast too hot. In some alloys it is possible to get a pale gilded colour when cast below 300°C. However, as the temperature increases, the oxide will gradually become darker, eventually gaining a slightly bluish tinge when it is certainly too hot.

If the casting is blotchy it is most probably dirty metal that has been used. The casting should be

Fig. VIII:59   *Showing the pattern, the first-stage plaster cast and the second-stage plaster cast, J. A. Murrell.*

Fig. VIII:60   *The final metal mould, cast from the second-stage plaster model, J. A. Murrell. (opposite)*

remelted and the mix fluxed and stirred and skimmed to remove the contamination.

Brittleness or breakage – cracking

Brittleness can be caused by ultra-slow cooling giving rise to a long crystal structure which is inherently weak – this is very unlikely to happen in normal circumstances.

Cracking can be caused by incorrect cooling between variations of section in the casting and also from metal that has been recast many times or from dirty metal. It is wise not to use too great a proportion of recast metal in any casting, below 50% if possible or less where intricate castings are required.

Fault checklist

Distortion and lack of detail:
  a Alloy – too hot, incorrect
  b Mould – shift, distorted, breakdown
  c In centrifugal casting – machine too fast.

Brittleness or breakage:
  a Alloy – incorrect, too cold, contaminated
  b Mould – poor, sections too thin
  c In centrifugal casting – machine too slow.

Flash:
  a Alloy – too hot
  b Mould – halves not clamped together.

Shifting:
a Mould – poor registration.

Porosity:
a Alloy – too hot, too cold, contains dross or otherwise contaminated
b Ingates too small, vents insufficient
c Mould – surface damaged
d Pattern – dirty
e In centrifugal casting – machine running too slow.

Cavity not filling:
a Alloy – too cold, insufficient quantity, poured too slowly
b Ingates too small, vents insufficient
c Mould – too cold
d In centrifugal casting – machine too slow.

Voids and blowholes:
a Alloy – too hot, too cold, incorrect, dirty
b Ingates and vents incorrect.

Roughness:
a Alloy – too hot, too cold, incorrect, dirty, contaminated
b Mould – dirty.

Discolouration:
a Alloy – too hot.

GENERAL HEALTH AND SAFETY

Safety measures when handling molten metals have already been discussed in the introduction.

With regard to the other materials used in the various processes described, none is particularly hazardous. However, the inhalation of fumes, plaster and sand dust is undesirable and therefore working areas should be kept clean and well-ventilated. All of the materials discussed have health and safety notes relating to them, either issued with the material or available from the supplier.

IX Finishing

INTRODUCTION

Finishing is the last process in the production of a piece of pewterware, but is by no means a technique tacked on to the end of the other processes. It is an art in itself, as it is the finish that determines the final appearance and characteristics of the piece of work. It must, therefore, be borne in mind both during the design and construction.

Finishing is sometimes loosely called polishing which is incorrect, as polishing is only one part of the complete process. There are in fact three stages known as (a) abrasive or cutting, (b) polishing, and (c) buffing or colouring.

The first stage of abrasive cutting, sometimes also described as bobbing or scurfing, uses abrasives to cut away the surface to remove irregularities and imperfection. The second stage of polishing uses very fine abrasives and smooths off the peaks by a combination of gentle cutting and frictional heat, which softens the metal and smears the peaks over the fine scratches, giving a bright smooth finish. The final stage of buffing or colouring is a gentle cleaning and burnishing process which gives an extremely fine, sometimes mirror finish, and brings out the colour of the metal.

EQUIPMENT

The basic piece of equipment is a polishing motor. These come in a range of sizes from as low as $\frac{1}{3}$ HP up to 5 HP or more, for the larger workshop. For the majority of the work undertaken in a pewter shop, a tapered motor spindle is most common because of the ease of fitting and removing polishing mops.

A wide range of mops is available and considerable advances in mop technology over the years have resulted in specialised types for particular jobs. The rate of surface removal and the type of effect produced are dependent upon the grade of polishing composition employed, the fabric from which the mop is made and the method of mop construction. A wide range of fabrics is used for the manufacture of polishing mops. Cotton mops range from soft unbleached cloths to special fast-cutting white fabrics incorporating special dressings. Sisal is used, either on its own in woven form or interleaved with cotton. Leather, chamois and felt mops are also available.

There are also a number of methods of mop construction, which in conjunction with the different materials give differing qualities to the mop. Open mops are made from whole discs of fabric with a centre assembly to hold them together. These mops present a very flexible surface to the work being polished. Stitched mops have the fabric discs stitched together with concentric rows of stitches, providing considerable stiffness to the mop. These are used for heavy duty polishing and are more easily dressed with abrasive compounds than flexible mops. Swansdown mops are very soft cotton unstitched mops for final polishing or colouring.

The mops screw on to the tapered thread of the polishing spindles, the thread cutting itself into the central hole of leather and cloth. The mops should be screwed on so that they run true and square. If not square on first time they should be taken off and screwed on again. Before use, the mop should be trued for concentricity and for removal of loose threads which could damage the work being polished. Trueing can be done with a stiff wire brush held against the rotating mop or alternatively a domestic cheese grater, which works very well.

As well as the disc mops, a number of different shaped mops in smaller diameters are available for internal polishing. Felt mops can be easily cut to shape for internal use and external use for getting into sharp corners or special sections. However, great care should be taken with felt mops on pewter as they cut relatively fast.

TECHNIQUE

The basic method of polishing pewter is the under-hand method, that is, the mop rotates with its top face running towards the operator and obviously the lower face rotates away from the operator. The work is held against the mop a few degrees below the horizontal centre line. The part of the surface being polished, or cut, is held tangential to the mop and the work is moved downwards at 45° across the mop. The work is moved also in the opposite direction to avoid lines being formed across the work. If the work is held too far down it is liable to be pulled out of the operator's hands. If too high, it tends to get knocked out of the operator's hands. The angle is correct when a constant and even controllable pull is felt. If the work piece has an open edge, then it should be fed in from the lower edge to halfway across. The work piece would then be turned around and the other half polished to the centre. The work piece should never be taken right across as there is the great danger of the mop grabbing the edge and tearing it out of the operator's hands.

No loose clothing such as shirtsleeves or ties should be free to catch in the rotating spindle. A protective smooth overall should be worn and preferably some eye protection. The stance should be comfortable and balanced with the feet well apart to give good body control. The work should be held in cupped hands where possible, for example, no

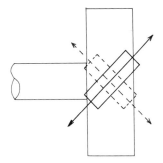

Diag. IX:2 *Showing general directions of movement of work relative to polishing mop.*

thumbs sticking through handles, so that if the work is grabbed by the mop it can slip easily out of the hands. There should be clear space around the machine for free movement and the bench or table clear of other tools or work. Ideally, some definite form of air and dust extraction should be fitted and the whole area well-ventilated and well-lit.

Abrasive cutting

The first stage in the process is the cutting stage using some form of abrasive compound. The traditional method in the pewter industry and one which most of the larger companies still use today, is to

Fig. IX:1 *Showing position of work relative to the mop in underhand polishing, Tether Manufacturing Ltd.*

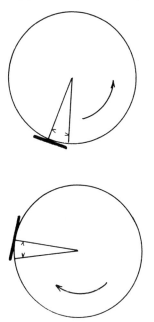

Diag. IX:1 *Polishing methods.*

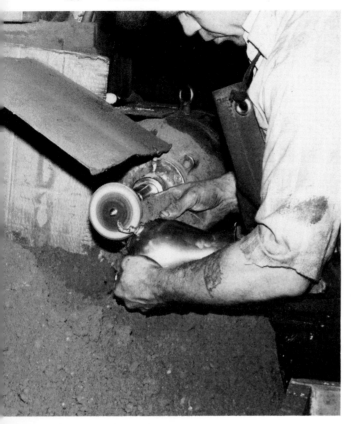

use a mixture of Trent sand and vegetable oil. The fine sand is dampened with a vegetable oil and is heaped in a tray below the mop. The mop is usually a firm stitched mop of brown unbleached cloth, dressed white fabric or sisal. The operator scoops up the sand and drops it in between the mop and the work. The oily sand sticks to the mop for a while before the mop needs recharging. Pumice powder is also used, mixed with sand and oil. The abrasive action of the sand is quite fierce and care must be taken not to remove too much metal. The sand method, whilst being very efficient, is very dirty and is not really suitable for the small workshop. It is also preferable to keep this first stage away from succeeding stages as any sand contaminating polishing mops would spoil the work.

An alternative to loose sand is to use an abrasive compound in stick form or applied by brush to coat the mop. The compounds are either emery or silicone carbide powder mixed with a binder which adheres to the mop. The composition is supplied in stick form and is applied to the mop simply by holding the stick against the rotating mop.

The cutting action of mops coated with abrasive depends upon the surface speed of the mop. A 150 mm (6 in.) diameter mop running at 2,900 rpm will give a surface speed of 23 m/sec. (4,550 ft/min.) which is generally regarded as the best speed for cutting. At higher speeds a brighter finish is given, but the cutting action is diminished. Abrasive materials and compounds are classified in grit sizes or mesh sizes and a common range is from 240 at the fine end to 60 at the coarse end. In the case of pewter it is unlikely that much above mid-range is needed initially, and then successively finer grades are used until the desired finish is attained.

A further method of abrasive cutting is to use endless belts. These are thin fabric belts coated with abrasive ranging from 320 to 24 mesh. The abrasive is mostly fused aluminium oxide and is bonded to the belt by glue or synthetic resin. The polishing procedure is exactly the same as using a mop, though the belt, even with a flexible contact wheel, will not be quite as flexible as a mop alone and it may be difficult to get into awkward recesses.

Matt and satin finish

A lot of pewterware is actually finished at the first stage without the second stage of polishing. Matt and satin finishes are within the first-stage process of abrasive cutting.

Fig. IX:2 *First stage abrasive cutting using sand, PMC Ltd, Sheffield.*

Fig. IX:3 *Abrasive cutting with an endless belt, A. E. Williams.*

The procedure is a continuation of the abrasive cutting using finer and finer abrasives. All large scratches and surface marks should be removed in the early stages prior to the final satin finish. Special compounds have been developed for this process superceding the older and messy method of wet pumice and brush wheels. The compound is applied to a soft cloth mop until the surface is well-coated. Very light pressure is used to obtain the finish and unlike the cutting procedure, the work is moved in line with the mop so that the scratch lines follow the contours of the article. Some experience is necessary to get a perfect finish with all the scratch lines parallel and conforming to the shape of the article. The light touch, however, does mean that errors can be covered up fairly easily. The mop should be kept well-charged with compound to avoid missing areas and uneven scratches. An ideal surface speed is 24 m/sec. (5,000 ft/min.), that is a little faster than cutting. An important feature is the greaseless nature of the compound and no further cleaning other than a detergent wash is required, thus reducing the possibility of damage to the satin finish.

An alternative method of applying a satin finish is by the use of Scotchbrite mops, by 3M Company. Scotchbrite is a chemical-resistant material of tough fibres, to which fine, evenly distributed abrasive mineral grains are resin bonded. The material is available in a number of grades, the most suitable for pewter being Very Fine A and Medium A. A low surface speed is recommended and very light pressure. A 100 mm (4 in.) diameter mop at 2,900 rpm gives a surface speed of 15 m/sec (3,100 ft/min.) which is ideal. The material is used dry and gives a greaseless finish, so only detergent washing is required.

A further method to produce a matt or satin finish is by the use of wire brushing, which will also produce a frosted surface. As far as pewterware is concerned, the technique has in the main been superceded by the two methods previously described.

Generally, for satin and matt finishes, it is better to continue the abrasive cutting stage, by using smaller and smaller grit sizes, beyond the level required, i.e. more polished, and then cut the surface back to the satin or matt finish required. This will ensure that all deep scratches have been removed and it is also easier to control the appearance by working back from a smooth surface. It is sometimes the practice to satin-finish by hand using similar materials as used in machine-polishing. Alternatively, very fine abrasive sheets of silicone

Fig. IX:4   *Hand-polishing with a stone leaf. (Photo: Selangor Pewter Co., Malaysia)*

carbide, often known as wet and dry can be used. Wire or steel wool used with light pressure is also very effective. An intriguing method employed in Malaya is to hand-finish with a leaf, called a stone leaf. This has a very fine hard abrasive surface, hence its name, and is simply plucked from bushes growing in the nearby jungle.

Polishing

This is the second stage in the finishing process and the stage where the scratches from the previous stage are removed by finer cutting compound. Tripoli is a form of amorphous silica with good abrasive qualities which is mixed with a special grease to form a bar or block. Different grades and qualities are available, Lustre, Crown, Star, Diamond and Lion. The highest quality is Lustre and this is the most suitable for use with pewter.

The mop should be of soft unbleached cloth and for most pewterware preferably an unstitched mop should be used as it has more flexibility to suit contoured work. Surface speed should be high to give a good polishing action. A 200 mm (8 in.) diameter

Fig. IX:5   *Using a soft flexible mop to polish contoured work, PMC Ltd, Sheffield.*

Fig. IX:6   *Internal polishing, Tether Manufacturing Ltd. (opposite)*

Buffing or colouring

This is the third stage of the finishing process, to give a clean high gloss or mirror-like finish.

The process is gentle and the mops and general area must be free from contamination of other abrasives or polishes. The compound used in this stage is either a rouge composition or a white polish based on whiting. Rouge is made from red oxide in varying grades of fineness mixed with a special grease. A very fine rouge is Radio or AA which comes in bar form. Alternatively, rouge can be purchased in powder form and mixed with water or methylated spirit. The white polish known as Peerless polish is an alternative.

For this process, a very soft mop known as a Swansdown mop is used. Surface speed is similar to polishing, but pressure is very light. The compound is applied as before and buffing carried in one direction across the surface. After buffing, the work should be washed gently in a detergent and carefully dried to prevent scratching the surface. Hot-air drying is recommended with a final rub using a jeweller's cloth prior to packing or use.

SUMMARY

It can be seen that many variations of finish are available and a considerable range of mops and compounds in different combinations will give different appearances. Only trial and error and experience will determine the exact requirements to suit the individual pewtersmith.

CARE AND MAINTENANCE

Having attained a finish to the article in keeping with its use and design, it is desirable to maintain this appearance. With modern pewter the tarnishing effect of normal atmosphere is almost negligible. Consequently, washing in soapy water or a mild detergent is all that is normally required. The use of a dishwasher is not to be recommended because of the very high water temperature and usually rather strong detergents. After washing, the article should be dried with a soft cloth and when completely dry, given a gentle polish with a soft duster.

Articles in constant use will eventually lose any original high polish because of the minute scratches caused by handling. This will give a used but attractive appearance which is very acceptable. There is in

mop running at 2,900 rpm gives a suitable speed of 30 m/sec. (6,200 ft/min.). The Tripoli bar is applied to the rotating mop to give a good coating, making sure that it is evenly spread across the surface. Polishing generally requires lighter pressure than cutting and the work should be moved across the mop so that the polishing is in one direction only. Polish towards the centre then turn the work around and polish back towards the centre again. Where the polishing overlaps at the centre, the work should be feathered off by gradually reducing the pressure. The action should be continued until all scratches have been blended in. If any deep scratches were missed in the first stage, they will show up clearly. Should the scratch be very deep, it is better to go back to the first stage rather than attempt to polish it out. When the work starts collecting smudges, it is time to recharge the mop with compound, as the smudges are grease, the abrasive having broken down. If the surface of the mop appears hard and glazed, it should be raked-out or cleaned with the cheese grater or wire brush. Polishing should continue until the work has an even appearance all over, without odd areas of dullness or high gloss. Care should be taken when working under and around handles and a soft unstitched flexible mop should be used so that its discs can flap into these areas.

Work can be left at this stage and regarded as finished if the appearance is as desired. Washing in a detergent will remove all traces of compound, but careful drying is necessary to avoid marking or scratching the newly polished surface.

fact some argument here with regard to the initial high polish given to articles of everyday use, such as tankards, by some manufacturers. It may well be worth considering that with this type of article an initial satin finish is preferable as this will not show up scratches caused by everyday wear and tear to the same extent.

CLEANING ANTIQUE PEWTER

Cleaning is usually one of the first matters on which guidance is sought and although it is not necessarily the first operation to be carried out in the course of restoration, it is appropriate that a section should be devoted to it.

There are different opinions as to whether, and to what extent, pieces should be cleaned, and the final decision must rest with the owner. My own view is that cleaning should be carried out to the extent that the pieces have sufficient polish to show at least some reflected light. Black unpolished pewter adds nothing to the appearance of a room, and pieces soon lose their outline in the shadows, becoming almost invisible in certain lights.

Before dealing with the somewhat messy business of removing scale, I would emphasise strongly that certain pewter alloys, generally those containing a comparatively high quantity of lead, such as the metal used for balusters and, often, for Charles I flagons (say 1615–1640), rarely need descaling but often need fairly frequent cleaning, initially with a household metal polish. These pieces, if they have not been kept polished, often assume a dark grey colour, which however, is not akin to scale. After pieces of this nature have been kept in a warm room for a few

months and frequently polished with metal polish, they assume a very attractive appearance, still darkish grey but with a gleam of metal showing through. For these pieces no further cleaning is necessary other than an occasional rub with a duster and perhaps an annual cleaning with metal polish. A little extra effort to give a high polish to the finials, edges of the handles, the mouldings and the fillets enhances their appearance considerably.

Scale, however, is an entirely different problem. Basically, it is caused by oxidisation of the tin, due to cold, damp and general neglect, assisted by dust and dirt and possibly by chemical action of food or wine stains left on the piece when it was last used. The first step with any piece of this nature is to wash it well in hot water with detergent. The next step is to cover such parts of the piece as you do not wish to descale, for instance the back of a plate or the bottom of a flagon, with oil or Vaseline. The chemical used to dissolve the scale is caustic soda, and it should be mixed with cold water in accordance with the instructions on the tin. In the case of a plate or charger, the mixture can actually be made in the well of the piece itself. Rubber gloves should always be worn for this operation. Thus clad, one can use a piece of rag to spread the solution over parts to be cleaned. For descaling a plate or dish the well and the booge, in so far as they are immersed in the liquid, will take care of themselves, but the rim and the remainder of the booge may require frequent applications of the liquid with the aid of a piece of rag. When the surface of the piece has been well-covered, it should be left for, say, 24 hours. The part being treated should then be washed with clean water and the process repeated until all the scale has been removed.

The condition of the surface then revealed may be at first sight somewhat disappointing. It varies according to the thickness of the scale and the alloy of which the piece is made. Early metal containing copper will usually only form a thin scale, which when removed, leaves a fairly good surface, but some of the later metals form scale of different thicknesses, and the surface revealed may be uneven.

The next step, after thorough washing to remove all traces of the caustic soda, is to restore the surface. Before proceeding to this, however, one must consider the question of corrosion as distinct from scale. Corrosion can arise from many sources, but most frequently seems to derive from impurities, dirt, chemicals or dross in the original metal. These impurities, with the passage of time and the action of the atmosphere, attack the surrounding metal and often appear in the form of pustules on the surface, which when pierced with a sharp tool, generally reveal a grey powdery dust which has to be removed and replaced by new metal. If this is not done, the impurities continue to spread and destroy the surrounding metal. The corrosion can also spread between surfaces of the metal, and is often not detectable except for a comparatively small spot, and it is only when this is pierced that the extent of the corrosion is discovered. It is important to note that if these corrosion spots go right through the metal they should be cleaned out and filled with metal before using the caustic soda which may otherwise disfigure the back of the plate or the inside of a piece of holloware. A word of warning is perhaps desirable about pieces made of some of the later Britannia-type metals. The thin black scale which often forms on these is very difficult to remove and when removed reveals a surface which is extremely hard to polish.

STANLEY SHEMMEL

ELECTROLYTIC CLEANING

Since the oxide patina on pewter is formed by oxidation, it can be removed by reduction. Very slow reduction of oxidised bronzes can reduce the patina back to coherent metal, but I have not begun to achieve this with pewter.

Electrolytic stripping is, however, simple, clean, controllable to some extent and avoids the use of strong solutions of deleterious chemicals. As carried out by the following method the technique can result in the complete stripping of a heavily oxidised surface in 2 to 3 hours. This is achieved by making the pewter the cathode by connecting it to the negative wire of an ordinary car battery charger and immersing it in an electrolyte which contains an anode connected to the positive wire, and passing a current of 2 to 3 amps. A suitable electrolyte is a very dilute solution of caustic soda or washing soda (or any other indifferent salt) – about a teaspoonful to a bucket of water – the concentration being adjusted to give the required current flow. This also depends on the area of, and separation between, the cathode and the anode.

The stripping is directional and takes place on the surface of the pewter facing the anode. If the anode is a sheet of tin plate positioned say half an inch from the top face of a pewter plate only that face will be stripped. The separation between the anode and the pewter plate can be achieved by placing a thin slab of foamed plastic between them to make a sandwich. Make sure, however, that the foam is one with interconnecting 'bubbles', i.e. that it will mop up water like a sponge. If on the other hand the pewter piece is a pot and the anode is a metal container holding the electrolyte stripping will take place over the whole surface and if the pot is suspended centrally it will be uniformly cleaned. Varying the geometry of the anode and the separation, and stopping at the appropriate time will result in local or partial stripping.

There will be much frothing due to hydrogen production, a sludge will form and the anode, if it be tin plate, will emerge in a very rusty state. Do not be dismayed; but *do not smoke!*

It is well to be on the safe side, though only harmless low voltage should be present in the stripping bath, and disconnect the charger from the mains before putting your hands in the bath. Electricity plus water can be dangerous!

RONALD F. HOMER

X Decorative Techniques

INTRODUCTION

There are a number of techniques available and in current use for imparting decorative finishes to pewter. For convenience, these will be classified under four main headings (a) decoration by raising the surface of the metal, (b) decoration by removal of metal, (c) roller printing and (d) plain surface finishes. It will be found in practice that techniques overlap and in many cases the final decoration falls into more than just one category. However, in order to explain the techniques, the above categories will be used in the following text.

DECORATION BY RAISING THE SURFACE

Under this heading fall the processes of Repoussé, Chasing, Embossing and Stamping. Although strictly speaking these are quite separate techniques, they do in fact overlap and interchange very much. In simplistic terms it may be taken that repoussé is working mainly from the reverse side or back of the metal, chasing is working mainly from the front and embossing is similar to repoussé except that often a complete design is raised by using a preformed punch or die.

Chasing and repoussé

This is the technique of decorating the surface of the metal by indentation with specially shaped punches. No metal is removed and the pattern will be visible on both sides of the metal. When produced in low relief it is described as flat chasing. It is, however, also produced in high relief by bossing up the surface initially and then indenting back as required by the design. The technique is also used to sharpen cast decoration and for texturing and shading. The experienced chaser will probably have a hundred or more punches, many of which have been specially made to suit a particular design. Punches are available commercially, consisting of sets of up to 30 or 40 punches. The hammer used with the punches is of a specialised design, being light in weight (120 g, 4 oz) with a small ball pein and a large convex face. The shaft is very thin and springy, usually of lancewood, with a large ball-shaped end. The ball shape fits in the palm of the hand and is held rather loosely. The hammer is used from the wrist rather than the arm and tends to rotate in the palm of the hand, the shaft sliding through the fingers. This loose action gives perfect control over the force of the blow on the punch and consequently the punch on the metal.

In order to carry out the work of chasing a design or pattern the pewter needs to have some form of resilient backing for the tools to work against. For flat sheet work a lead backing block is

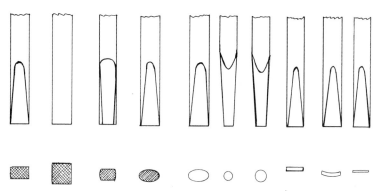

Diag. X:1 *Selection of repoussé/chasing punches.*

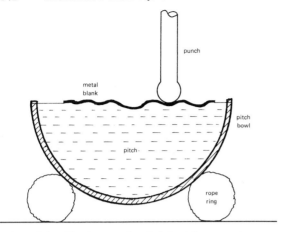

Diag. X:2 *Showing use of a pitch bowl for repoussé or chasing.*

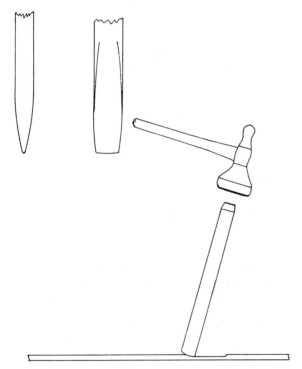

Diag. X:3 *Showing a tracer tool and the method of use.*

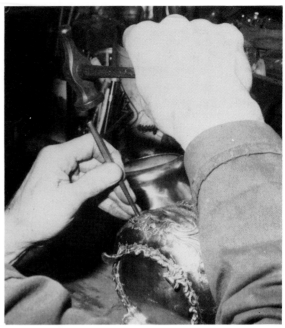

Fig. X:1 *Chasing a design on a hollow vessel, James Dixon & Sons Ltd.*

of pitch, eight parts of plaster, one part of resin and one part of linseed oil. The pitch should be melted in an iron pot and when molten, the plaster and other ingredients mixed in. Care should be taken not to overheat the pitch as it is inflammable. Once molten, the pitch can be poured into the mould. For large flat work the mould can be a simple wooden frame, somewhat larger than the sheet of pewter and approximately 18 mm ($\frac{3}{4}$ in.) thick. For smaller work a small hemispherical iron bowl is most suitable, as the bowl can be positioned in a rope ring and angled to any position. With hollow work the vessel itself must be filled with the pitch mixture after any required bossing-up has been done.

The sheet of metal should be pressed into the pitch whilst it is still warm and soft. The surface of the sheet should be smeared with vaseline or grease and then the sheet should be pressed well into the pitch. Broad areas of the design and those of high relief should be hammered in whilst the pitch is still warm and soft. Fine detail is best left until the pitch has set firm so that the design and shading can be clearly and sharply defined.

The design, or pattern, can be transferred to the metal by drawing direct with a pencil or a felt pen. Alternatively, a design may be transferred via a sheet of carbon paper by tracing, or a design can be pricked through with a sharp scriber leaving a series

quite suitable though it should be remelted and recast before use to give a flat smooth working surface. An alternative is to use a pitch block moulded into a frame. For hollow work, pitch is used to fill the cavity as it must be melted out after use.

Pitch alone is too hard and brittle and therefore it needs to be mixed with other substances to give it the necessary resilience. A suitable recipe is six parts

Diag. X:4 *Use of a snarling iron to raise surface of a hollow vessel.*

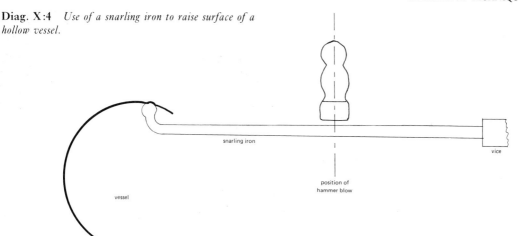

of dots to be followed. The experienced professional chaser will be found to be very much of an artist as well as a craftsman, and often works only to a very broad outline, chasing in the design as he goes. For the less experienced it is preferable to draw the design in considerable detail as once a mark has been made with a punch it is very difficult to erase it.

In use the punches are kept on the move with light successive taps rather than blows. Tracer punches for delineating are used at an angle, so that the lines are formed as a continuous line like drawing with a pen. Matting and texturing punches are normally held at right angles to the particular surface so that the texture design is transferred evenly. On flat sheets, large areas of high relief can be bossed up from the reverse side with a mallet on a sandbag prior to setting in the pitch tray or bowl. For hollow work such as pots, bowls and vases, a special tool is required to operate inside the vessel. The tool is known as a snarling iron and is a length of metal approximately 12 mm ($\frac{1}{2}$ in.) diameter and 45 cm (18 in.) long. One end is bent at right angles and is ball-ended. The straight end of the tool is clamped in a vice by one end, the vessel is held over the ball-end and the iron is struck halfway along its length with a hammer or iron bar. This causes the snarling iron to spring and the reaction at the ball-end raises the surface of the vessel. By varying the force of the blow and by moving the vessel as required, areas can be bossed-up to the shape desired.

It is essential that the articles being worked on are held firmly in position as both hands are in use, one holding the punch and one holding the hammer. If the work moves when the punch is struck with the hammer, damage is liable to occur. Flat work is

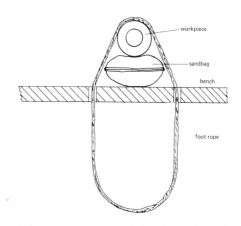

Diag. X:5 *Showing method of clamping workpiece by the use of a foot rope.*

no problem if it is struck firmly in the pitch and the pitch is supported in a frame. If a pitch bowl is used for small flat work, it can be supported on sandbags or rope rings, the weight of the bowl itself aiding in this method of support. Holloware is more difficult to support and a technique used by many craftsmen is to support the work on one or more sandbags and clamp into position with a foot rope. Two holes are drilled through the workbench, one either side of the sandbags. A piece of small diameter rope is passed over the work and through the holes in the bench. The ends of the rope are tied to form a loop so that the craftsman's foot can set in the loop and push down thus clamping the work firmly against the sandbags.

When the work is complete it is removed from the pitch tray by heating the metal with a torch or, in the case of a hollow vessel, the pitch must be melted out. Final removal of grease and pitch can be

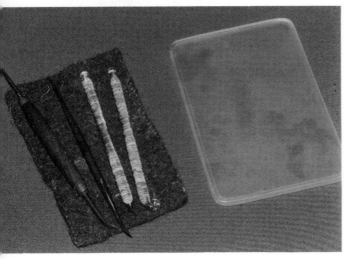

Fig. X:2 *Tools, felt and plate glass for repoussé work, Elise M. Ramsay.*
Fig. X:3 *Examples of repoussé work, Elise M. Ramsay. (opposite)*

carried out using paraffin or white spirit.

Work to be chased should be finish polished before starting so that only the minimum of cleaning and polishing is required at completion, otherwise there is the danger of buffing away some of the fine detail.

Chasing tools can be used to very good effect on cast designs by sharpening up the detail giving quite a different appearance from the 'as cast form'.

Repoussé – foil

This is work carried out mainly from the back and finished from the front by chasing. Thus repoussé and chasing go very much together and at times are difficult to separate. The tools are very similar and often interchangeable. All have slightly rounded edges to prevent digging into the metal, though repoussé punches tend to be rounded off more than chasing punches.

The use of the tools and equipment is virtually as described previously for chasing, particularly with regard to the heavier gauges of pewter sheet (see pp. 141–3).

Much of the present-day repoussé work is carried out using very light gauge pewter sheet and pewter foil. With this material very simple tools are required and quite intricate designs can be produced in foil for use as plaques, brooches, pendants and other such items. It can also be used to cover boxes of wood or other materials or used as part of an appliqué design.

Tools can be made from knitting needles, particularly the large wooden variety, or plasticine modelling tools can be used. The tools fall into the same categories as the professional punches, that is tracers, formers and shading or matting tools. The other requirement is a sheet of thick firm felt and a sheet of plate glass for finishing or chasing.

Designs can be traced or drawn on to the reverse side of the sheet of foil, remembering of course that the design should be the reverse of the desired frontal design. The piece of felt is laid on the sheet of glass and the sheet of pewter foil placed on the felt. The outline should be delineated first, using one or more of the tracer tools. Further areas are then raised with former tools to suit. The tools should be used with a strong action to avoid bumps and lumps. Once the pattern has been completed the foil is removed from the felt and then laid front side up on the plate glass. The design can then be sharpened up using tracers, and edge background areas stroked flat with a burnishing tool. Initially only simple designs should be attempted until experience is gained and the feel of the material is appreciated.

As designs become more complex, more and more specialised tools will be required. It is better to take time to make these relatively simple tools rather than attempt to use a tool that is not really the exact shape required.

As the material is relatively soft and weak, the raised areas need supporting before use. Good-quality plaster or barbola paste is ideal for this purpose, the depressions being filled and the back surface smoothed off.

Brooches, pendants and plaques can also be backed with pewter foil after the depressions have been filled with plaster. An allowance of $2\frac{1}{2}$ mm ($\frac{1}{10}$ in.) should be left all around the desired shape and worked up to a right angle. This can be done quite easily on a simple wooden stake shaped to suit. A backing plate cut exactly to shape is dropped in and the vertical edges folded over with a burnishing tool. This method of construction adds to the weight, gives rigidity and protects the plaster.

Embossing and stamping

Although embossing is basically similar to the raising or relief work as in chasing and repoussé, it is taken in this text to be specific to designs raised in one piece.

This may take the form either of a complete design on one punch or a design made up from a number of individual punches, each with a specific pattern. The design punch can be as simple as a piece of thick cardboard, wood or hardboard for use on pewter foil or made from steel or brass for thicker sheets. The edges of the design on the punch must be rounded off to prevent cutting the metal. For low relief work the sheet of metal may be placed on a pitch block or a lead block. The punch

can be struck with a hammer or alternatively the punch can be fitted into a fly press. For work of high relief it will be necessary to produce a mating block to avoid wrinkling of the sheet. This mating block must carry a negative impression of the punch. If the relief is not too high this mating block can be produced by pressing the punch into a block of lead, thus creating a matching impression. It may then be found necessary to reduce the outside dimensions of the punch to allow for the thickness of the pewter sheet.

If a number of sheets are to be embossed, then it is preferable to make the mating block of a harder material than lead. Pewter or aluminium can be cast around the punch to form a cast matching impression. The punch, which should be made from brass or steel, is placed in the centre of a small mould box and molten pewter or aluminium poured over it and allowed to cool.

Embossing or die-stamping of this nature is best carried out on a fly press and it is essential to position the punch or die exactly over the mating block, which should be fixed firmly on the base plate of the press.

If the pattern or design is complex and a steel punch or die is required, then it is unlikely that the production of this can be carried out in the pewter workshop. The assistance of a professional die-sinker will be required, but such dies will produce many thousands of items. However, for short run work

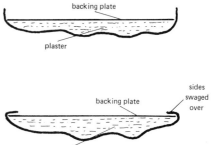

Diag. X:6 *Fitting a backing plate to a repoussé plaque or brooch.*

aluminium alloy dies can be produced by carving wax or plaster models and using these as moulds for casting, using the techniques described in the section on casting (pp. 90–133).

DECORATION BY REMOVAL OF METAL

Under this heading fall two basic methods of decoration by removal of metal, namely Engraving and Etching.

Hand engraving
Hand engraving is one of the oldest arts and is a combination of technical skill and high artistic ability. Its use on modern-day pewter is limited to the highly priced end of the market because of the

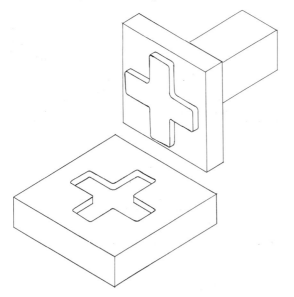

Diag. X:7   *Embossing die and punch.*

Fig. X:4   *The engravers' bench and equipment, O'Connell & Yardley.*

Fig. X:5   *A selection of gravers, James Dixon & Sons Ltd.*

time required to carry out the work and the high skill of the engraver.

The basic techniques for simple designs can, however, be learnt by the student, the amateur and professional pewtersmith whilst the more artistic work can be left to the skilled engraver.

The tools and equipment required are simple and relatively cheap. The basic requirements are a good bench of such a height to be comfortable when standing or sitting. A stool is preferable to a chair and it should be adjustable in height to allow an ideal working position. Two or three sandbags are required, including a ring, for supporting the work. It is essential that the lighting over the bench is adequate and if possible the bench should be positioned so that north light is available to restrict reflections in bright daylight.

The cutting tools are called gravers which are produced in a number of shapes to suit the style of cut required. The gravers are made from steel hardened and tempered and are approximately 100 mm (4 in.) long and of a 6 mm ($\frac{1}{4}$ in.) square section. Each graver is fitted with a mushroom-shaped handle to fit into the palm of the hand. To enable the tool to be used correctly, it is common practice to cut away part of the handle so that it is well clear of the work. As supplied, the graver has its cutting face ground off at an angle of 45°. This, in itself, is insufficient and before use the underside of the cutting face needs to be backed off by approximately 5° to 10°. This is called the set-off angle and compensates for the angle at which the tool is held, relative to the horizontal. Without this set-off angle, the tool would dig in and would not run along the bottom of the cut. The standard shapes, of which six are shown in diagram X:9, have been developed over the years, but like so many other crafts, special requirements demand special shapes and the skilled engraver builds up a collection of gravers. It is vitally important to keep the gravers sharp and a fine oil stone must always be available.

The technical skill in engraving is to achieve control over the tool, whereas the artistic skill is probably more of an inherent ability. However, the technical skill can be mastered by practice. It is better to practice using copper sheet rather than pewter, as copper is harder, closer grained and cuts cleaner. Pewter is soft, and initially the unskilled cut too deeply, and cast pewter is notorious for sudden grain change and hard and soft spots. The piece of copper plate should be smooth and polished and free of scratches or marks which could affect the cutting action of the tool.

The copper plate should be marked out with a

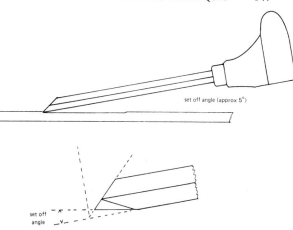

Diag. X:8 *Showing graver with set off.*

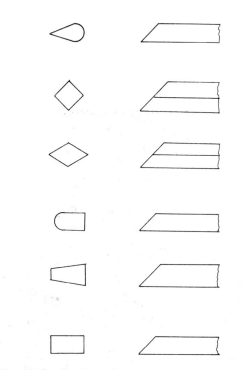

Diag. X:9 *Graving tools.*

few short scriber lines and initially a square graver should be chosen. The graver is held with the handle in the palm of the hand with the thumb lying along the left-hand edge of the graver and the first two fingers pressing against the other side. The point of the graver should project approximately 12–18 mm ($\frac{1}{2}$–$\frac{3}{4}$ in.) beyond the end of the thumb. The graver is driven by the pressure of the palm of the hand and not the arm. The thumb acts as a guide and a brake resting on the metal as the graver runs along the thumb pad. The graver is initially held at

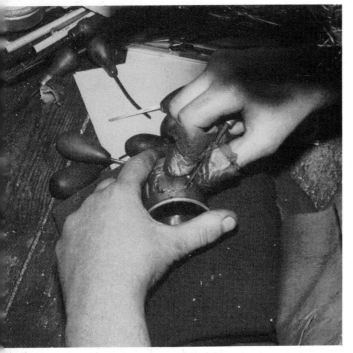

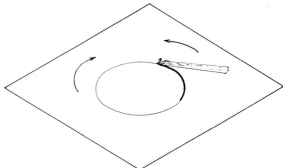

Diag. X:10   *Engraving a circle: the plate moves anti-clockwise and the graver moves clockwise.*

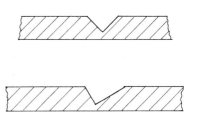

Diag. X:11   *Showing two common types of engraving cut.*

Fig. X:6   *Engraving a cup, James Dixon & Sons Ltd.*

approximately 45° and driven into the metal to the desired depth. The angle is then lowered to the set-off angle and then driven forward along the line. At the end of the cut the graver is flicked up taking the last piece of metal out of the cut. Circles are cut by using both hands, the left hand turning the work so that in effect the graver is cutting in a straight line with the work being turned into it. By rolling or rotating the wrist the shape of the cut can be varied by making one side wider than the other. Larger area cuts are made by using flat-edge and round-edge gravers. Cuts are also made wider by a process known as threading, which is done by a number of very fine cuts. It is this combination of various shaped tools, rolling and threading which gives hand engraving such an appeal. Close examination of high-quality hand engraving will show quite clearly the artistry and technical skill that goes into such work.

Designs can be applied to the metal in a number of ways. Original artwork can be copied by drawing or can be transferred. In order to draw on a polished surface, it can be dulled down with soft wax, which is then given a coating of french chalk dabbed on with cotton wool or a pounce bag. The design can then be drawn on using an orange stick or traced through the original artwork. The faint lines produced by the orange stick are then scribed in

with a metal scriber. Existing engravings can be transferred by filling them with soap, placing a piece of tissue paper over them and then gently rubbing the surface, which transfers the soap to the paper. The paper is placed on the new work and by gentle rubbing, the soap outline is transferred. This can then be scribed in by using a metal scriber.

The highly skilled professional engraver with high artistic ability very often uses guide lines or broad outlines only and actually draws the design.

Lettering and monogram work is a subject in itself for as well as the engraving skill required, a knowledge of the various scripts is also required. Similarly with crests and coats of arms, a considerable knowledge of heraldry is required in order to produce satisfactory and accurate work. Colours and furs used in heraldic work are represented by standard forms of shading or cut patterns, with specific patterns representing specific colours.

Polishing and buffing after engraving must be carried out with great care to avoid any rounding off of sharp edges which could destroy the whole effect.

Machine engraving

Machine engraving is in common use on pewter for two major reasons: it is less expensive than hand engraving and it is more suited for long production runs. Engraving by machine does not have the appeal of hand engraving as there is little subtlety in

the cut, however, it can produce pleasing and acceptable work at an economic price.

The machine is based on the pantograph principle and is substantially and accurately built, so that there is no slack in the system and reproduction is faithfully produced. Machines are available to give reproductions varying from one to one to sixteen to one. This means that relatively large original patterns can be made with considerable intricacies for finely detailed work on the finished item. The cutters are usually of pointed form which give a V-shaped cut. The cutter head is belt driven and speeds range from 3,000 rpm to 15,000 rpm depending upon the cutter and the material.

In use the original design, which may be standard-letter masters, commercially available, or hand-produced masters, is mounted at the back of the machine in a copy holder. The work piece is mounted on a table on the front of the machine. The worktable is adjustable up and down, left to right and front to back, so it is easy to centralise the

Fig. X:7 *Engraving heraldic designs, O'Connell & Yardley.*

work. A stylus is hand-operated to follow the master design and with the machine running, the worktable is raised to meet the cutter and fixed at the correct cut depth. The stylus is moved with a to-and-fro action following the master outline, until the work is complete.

For cylindrical work such as tankards, cups and goblets, a rotary head is available which can be mounted on the worktable. This is set so that the cutter works on the centre line of the work piece and the work piece is rotated to suit. Some considerable skill is required with cylindrical work in keeping the cut at a constant depth and calls for complete co-ordination of movement of stylus and rotating head.

The use of hand-cut masters and slight variations

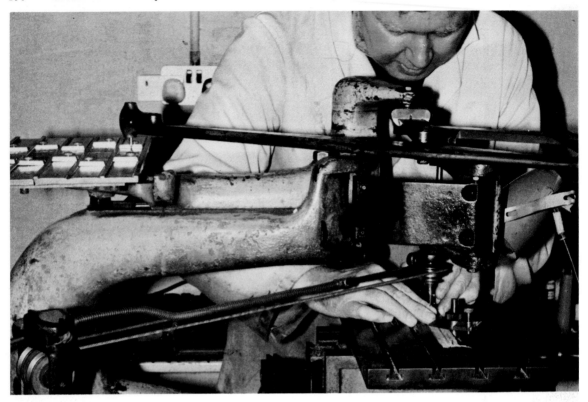

in cutter profile do in fact give machine engraving a flavour so that the machine-cut look is reduced. This is particularly apparent with regard to lettering, where a hand-cut master gives a much more acceptable final engraving, compared with using a standard commercial master.

Acid etching

This is a process for decoration by removal of metal where the metal is dissolved by an acid as opposed to being cut away mechanically with a tool.

The process is simple, requires little equipment and can be carried out in the pewter workshop provided normal precautions are taken with regard to the handling of acidic liquids.

Before preparing a design it is essential that the pewter sheet be free from grease or oil, so it should be cleaned off with a degreasing agent or washed in hot soapy water. An acid-resistant coating or ground is then applied to the surface of the metal. If the piece is small, then it can be covered all over, or if the design is in the centre of a large plate, then the ground should cover the design area plus 18 mm ($\frac{3}{4}$ in.) all round. This can be a proprietary ground known as an etching ball or beeswax or one of the modelling waxes. The plate should be warmed and possibly also the wax and a complete covering applied to the metal. The wax should be of such

hardness and texture that it can be cut through, leaving clean lines without ragged edges. The design is cut through the wax with a sharp scriber or a strong sewing needle held in a pin vice; old gramophone needles were ideal for this purpose. With care, quite intricate and delicate detail can be drawn in this manner. Designs can be transferred to the wax by drawing directly on it or by tracing through a drawing.

Once the design is complete the plate can be prepared for etching with an acid solution. If the piece is small, the whole plate can be immersed in the acid, but in order to prevent the acid attacking the edges and the back of the metal, these areas should be painted with varnish. An alternative, and essential with a large plate, is to build a wall around the design, using plasticine or wax. The wall should be approximately 9 mm ($\frac{3}{8}$ in.) high to avoid any overspill of acid solution. This method can also be used to etch designs on the surface of cylindrical items such as tankards or vases, though in this case it is preferable to build the wall higher to counteract the curvature. The wall method should also be used when etching the inside bottom of a bowl.

The acid solution can be either a nitric acid or hydrochloric acid solution. The nitric will produce blacker lines than the hydrochloric acid. A suitable

Fig. X:8 *Engraving machine, A. E. Williams. (opposite)*

Fig. X:9 *Items ready for etching (note letraset letters on cup); J. A. Murrell. (top)*

Fig. X:10 *Plasticine walls, built around areas to be etched, J. A. Murrell.*

solution is to mix one part of nitric acid to ten parts of water and add 3 or 4 grammes of copper sulphate, or some copper filings, which takes the vicious bite out of the acid. When mixing the solution, it is absolutely essential to add the acid to the water slowly and gently stir. Never under any circumstances add the water to the acid. Always wear rubber gloves and safety goggles when preparing the solution.

The solution should be poured into a plastic tray if the whole item is to be immersed, a photographers' developing dish is ideal for this as it has a lip so that the contents can easily be poured back into the bottle. If the plasticine wall method is being used, then the solution should be poured in to a depth of approximately 3 mm ($\frac{1}{8}$ in.).

The etching time depends on the strength of the solution and the temperature. Strong solutions act faster and give sharper edges to the design. Weaker solutions tend to give more rounded edges. The exact time can only be determined by experience and the desired depth of the etch, though it is only a matter of minutes. Initially the work should be removed after 2 minutes, washed off and the etch examined for depth. Based on this, the desired time can be estimated.

For one-off items, or occasional use, a very

simple and cheap method is to use a commercially available etching kit designed for producing prototype printed circuit boards. The kit consists of a bottle of etching fluid and a fibre-tipped pen containing a special acid-resistant ink. Designs are drawn directly on the pewter sheet with the pen. If the design is to be in relief then the design is drawn or if the design is to be etched then the background is filled in. For lettering or initials, instant print such as Letraset can be used. The letters are applied exactly as if they were being applied on paper or artwork. Provided the metal is clean, the letters adhere well and are acid resistant. Using a combination of Letraset and the special pen, plaques, name plates and etched designs can be produced in a few minutes. The etching fluid, like the acid solutions, are reusable and should be poured back into the bottle. Obviously the life of the solution depends upon the amount of metal to be etched away each time, but as a rough guide, a 250 ml (9 oz) bottle of etching fluid will produce some 40 or more designs of 25 mm (1 in.) square.

After etching, the item should be washed in running water and then washed in a detergent or washing-up fluid. The resist ground is removed with a solvent, like white spirit, and the item buffed or polished to suit, care being taken not to spoil the etching.

Photo-etching

This is a method of etching by using an electrolytic

Fig. X:11   *Photo-resist stencils, A. E. Williams.*

Fig. X:12   *Dabbing the stencil on a plate, A. E. Williams.*

Fig. X:13   *Showing the completed etching, A. E. Williams.*

process through a photo-resist stencil.

The stencil is produced photographically from original artwork. The artwork is drawn many times full size so that very fine detail may be included. The master artwork is photographically reduced on to a transparency using a high-precision camera. The transparency is reprinted on to a sensitised stencil made from very fine nylon mesh. After processing, the stencil is resistant to the electrolyte except where the design lines were reproduced. The stencil is positioned on the item to be etched and taped in position.

The equipment consists of a transformer to convert AC current to DC, two leads, a base plate and a carbon block. The positive lead is connected to the metal baseplate, upon which the item to be etched is positioned so that it makes good electrical contact. The negative lead is attached to the carbon block, which is fitted with a handle. A piece of absorbent felt is wrapped around the carbon block. The felt is soaked in an electrolyte made up from salts, water and a wetting agent. Surplus electrolyte is wiped off the felt pad and the electric power switched on via a rheostat. The damp felt and carbon block is pressed or dabbed onto the stencil and the current adjusted to 20–30 amps. The block is dabbed over the whole design in a continuous manner and pewter will pass through the stencil onto the felt pad. The action is rapid, and within $1\frac{1}{2}$ to 2 minutes lines will be etched in the pewter to a considerable depth leaving a very well-formed design exactly as the stencil. As the process is very fast it is essential to keep the carbon block continually dabbing so that the design is etched to an even depth. Care must be taken also not to go beyond the edges of the stencil, otherwise the item will be damaged.

Upon completion, the stencil is removed and the item cleaned with some of the electrolyte and then immediately washed in a detergent. The stencil is rinsed in a dilute hydrochloric acid solution which removes any pewter in the nylon mesh. Similarly, the felt pad is washed ready for reuse. Stencils can be used 50 or more times before replacement. The etching can be left as etched, with a dark grey appearance, or can be inked in with a hard-drying black ink.

The equipment is available commercially and the process is easy to use and because of the extreme accuracy of the photographic process, very fine and intricate designs are possible.

ROLLER PRINTING

There is a considerable market for tankards bearing sporting designs such as golfing, hunting, football scenes, etc. The costs of hand engraving or machine engraving such items would be excessive where items of relatively low value are being treated. Consequently, a technique of roller printing has been developed. Pewter lends itself to this process as it is a soft material and provided the article can be produced by rolling up from a flat sheet, a satisfactory and acceptable appearance can be produced. The finished work does not have the aesthetic appeal of engraved work, but many of the scenes and designs are extremely well drawn and can look very attractive.

The process is in fact similar to printing where a patterned die is rolled under pressure over a flat sheet. The die plate is photo-etched from original artwork, but in this case it is the background that is etched away, leaving a line diagram. The die plate is then electroplated with a very hard material such as chrome, so that the raised lines are now relatively hard.

Precut blanks of pewter are attached to the die plate, or located accurately upon it, and the assembly passed between a set of rolls. The rolls are power driven and adjustable for height and pressure to suit the die plate thickness. The design is thus pressed into the sheet of pewter by this pressure and rolling action. The depth of the design is such that it can withstand the burnishing and polishing that must take place during the manufacture of the tankard or similar item. Quite complex detail and lettering can be reproduced by this method and, because the pewter is soft, die life is very long.

By a similar process it is also possible to produce slightly raised patterns, simulating hammered finish or planish marks. Again, these do not have the aesthetic appeal of true hammering or planishing, but a number of satisfactory design patterns are produced which suit the relative market. Blanks produced in this manner must of course be used in the production of articles where further working is minimised, to avoid the risk of damage to a design or pattern.

PLAIN SURFACE TREATMENT

Except for the normal polished finishes of either highly reflective or satin finishes, there are a number of other surface treatments available. Some pewter work forms the basis of silver plate work as in electroplated Britannia metal (EPBM), but that is outside the scope of this book, as it is part of the silversmiths' industry.

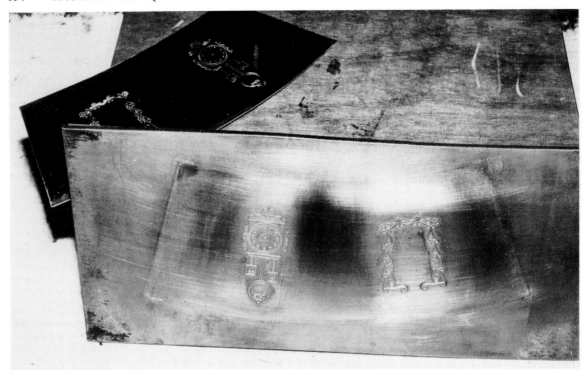

Fig. X:14   *The die plate with the raised line design, Tether Manufacturing Ltd.*

Fig. X:15   *The pewter blank with the impressed design, Tether Manufacturing Ltd.*

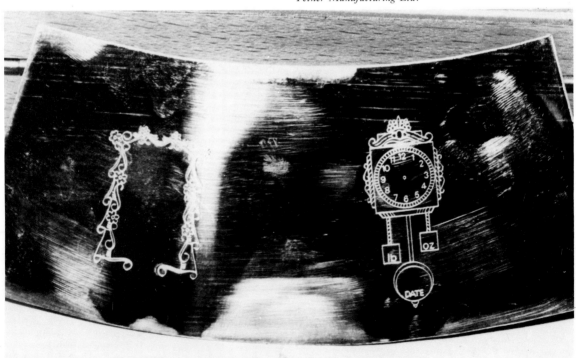

Chemical treatment

A common surface treatment is to darken the appearance or simulate an antique appearance, which is evident on old pewter because of the lead content. This darkening is applied chemically by dipping the articles in various solutions. Some solutions are available commercially, but can be readily made up. A number of formulae are in use, but all contain acid and therefore full safety precautions must be taken. Always add the acid to the water, and wear protective clothing, rubber gloves and safety goggles.

Formulae:

Blue-black patina	2.5 g copper sulphate
	50 ml nitric acid
	950 ml water
Brown-black patina	80 g arsenious oxide
	40 g copper sulphate
	5 g ammonium chloride
	450 ml hydrochloric acid
	500 ml water
Grey-black patina	100 ml sulphuric acid
	15 ml nitric acid
	900 ml water
	OR
	8 g copper chloride
	8 g copper nitrate
	8 g ammonium chloride
	100 ml hydrochloric acid
	950 ml water

The solutions are used cold.

The work to be coloured must be clean and grease-free before immersion. A degreasing solvent should be used and the work cleaned with a paste of whiting and then rinsed clean with water.

The items are then completely immersed in the solution, preferably being held in a rack which can be passed to the rinsing area after colouring. Colour intensity is time-dependent and immersion times vary from approximately 1 to 4 minutes. After colouring, the items should immediately be rinsed in running water and allowed to dry thoroughly.

The patina obtained can be buffed off fairly easily, so for permanence it is normal to apply a wax polish. Some of the patina can be deliberately buffed off on relief work or high spots so that they stand out against the dark background.

Lacquering and plating

A number of other treatments are available, such as gilding, bronzing and lacquering, though not in common use on pewter in the Western hemisphere. Some work from the East is made very attractive by the combination of the natural colour of pewter set against a coloured lacquered or deposited background.

Electroplating invariably demands the use of cyanide salts and specialised plant and equipment which is outside the scope of the small pewter workshop. However, a number of lacquers are available which are relatively easy to apply and are not subject to cellulose or petroleum regulations. Some lacquers can be used on water-wetted articles so that lacquering can take place immediately after cleaning and washing. The articles are lacquered by dipping and are then air dried or stove dried.

Special self-relieving lacquers are also available and relatively easy to use. The articles are sprayed with the lacquer, which can be tinted in a wide range of colours including shades of gold and bronze, and the pigments migrate through the lacquer to collect in the indentations leaving the high spots protected by clear lacquer showing their natural colour.

Glossary

Amalgam   A compound or union of different metals
Backstick   A hardwood rod used in conjunction with the forming tool in the spinning operation
Booge   The radiused section between the base and the rim of a plate
Burnish   To polish pewter surface using a polished steel tool
Chasing   A method by which a design is produced on an object by indenting or raising the surface; no metal is removed
Chill blocks   Small block of metal, usually aluminium or pewter, inserted into rubber mould to assist cooling
Chuck   A tool mounted on the headstock to hold the piece to be worked on; in pewter working, this is often a wooden or plastic former shaped to suit the shape of the piece to be machined or formed
Cope   The upper box of a pair of mould boxes
Core   The part of a mould which provides the internal shape to a hollow casting
Core print   The areas provided in the external parts of a mould to hold and locate the core when producing hollow castings
Dowel pin   Locating pin
Drag   The lower box of a pair of mould boxes
Draw spike   A screwed rod used for withdrawing the pattern when making a sand mould
Dross   Oxide and other impurities which form on the surface of the molten metal in the melting pot
Embossing   A method of decorating by raising the surface
Engraving   A method by which a design is produced on an object by cutting and removing metal
Fettle   To clean a casting by removing the flash or sprue prior to the final finishing process
Freeman   A pewterer on completing his seven-year apprenticeship was made 'free' of the Worshipful Company of Pewterers; as a freeman, he was entitled to work as a journeyman for a master pewterer or, with the permission of the Company, set up in business on his own
Frustum   The part of a conical shape formed by cutting off the top in a plane parallel to the base
Fulcrum pin   The pin fitted into the tool rest to support the levering action of the forming tool in the spinning operation

Gadrooning   Fluted, rounded moulding produced by casting, chasing or repoussé work
Headstock   The rotating spindle of the lathe on to which can be fitted a faceplate or chuck for holding the piece to be worked on
Hypotenuse   The side of a right-angled triangle that is opposite the right angle
Journeyman   A pewterer who has served his apprenticeship and works for a master pewterer
Mandrel   A spindle on to which a chuck or the piece to be worked, is fitted for turning in the lathe
Pantograph   An instrument of four rigid links jointed in a parallelogram form to copy designs to a predetermined scale
Patina   A dark colouring of pewter caused by the gradual oxidation over a long period of time or by the use of chemicals when wishing to simulate aging
Planish   To smooth or polish by hammering
Repoussé   Method of producing decoration on an object by initially beating up (raising) from the inside and thereafter using chasing techniques to produce the pattern
Snarling iron   A right-angled forming tool used for raising metal in repoussé and chasing techniques
Sprue   The part of a casting where the metal has been fed when filling the mould – it is normally removed prior to the cleaning-up process
Sprue hole   Hole through which the metal is poured when casting
Stake   A hard metal polished former of various shapes fitted to a wrought-iron shank used for forming metal sheet; held in a vice or special support fitted to bench
Tacking   Spot soldering
Tailstock   The adjustable head for the lathe for holding the 'centre' which supports the piece held in the headstock
Trammel   An instrument for drawing ellipses
Wrigglework   A type of engraving achieved by rocking a small chisel-shaped tool from side to side to achieve a zig zag pattern

Tables and Conversions

CONVERSION FACTORS

Imperial to metric
Inches × 25.399 = millimetres
Inches × 2.540 = centimetres
Feet   × 0.3048 = metres
Sq. inches × 645.16 = sq. millimetres
Sq. inches × 6.452 = sq. centimetres
Sq. feet   × 0.0929 = sq. metres
Cu. inches × 16.387 = cu. millimetres
Cu. inches × 0.0164 = litres
Ounces   × 28.35 = grammes
Pounds   × 453.6 = grammes
Pounds   × 0.4536 = kilogrammes
Pounds per sq. foot × 4.883 = kilos per sq. metre

Metric to imperial
Millimetres   × 0.0394 = inches
Centimetres   × 0.3937 = inches
Metres   × 39.37 = inches
Metres   × 3.28   = feet
Sq. millimetres × 0.00155 = sq. inches
Sq. centimetres × 0.155 = sq. inches
Sq. metres   × 10.764 = sq. feet
Cu. centimetres × 0.06102 = cu. inches
Grammes   × 0.03527 = ounces
Kilogrammes   × 35.3   = ounces
Kilogrammes   × 2.2046 = pounds
Kilos per sq. metre × 0.2048 = pounds per sq. foot

Temperature

$$\text{Fahrenheit} = \left(\frac{9 \times C^\circ}{5} \right) + 32^\circ$$

$$\text{Centigrade} = \left(\frac{F^\circ - 32^\circ}{9} \right) \times 5$$

°C	°F
0	32
10	50
20	68
30	86
40	104
50	122
60	140
70	158
80	176
90	194
100	212
120	248
140	284
160	320
180	356
200	392
220	428
240	464
260	500
280	536
300	572
320	608
340	644
360	680
380	716
400	752
420	788
440	824
460	860
480	896
500	932

PEWTER ALLOYS

Standard specification	Tin % Sn	Antimony % Sb	Copper % Cu	Lead % Pb
BS 5140: 1974	at least			
Alloy A	91	5–7	1.0–2.5	0.5
	at least			
Alloy B	93	3–5	1.0–2.5	0.5
DIN 17810: 1974				
Sn Sb2 Cu 1.5	balance	1.0–3.0	1.0–2.0	max 0.5
Sn Sb5 Cu 1.5	balance	3.7–7.0	1.0–2.0	max 0.5
ASTM B 560				
Type 1	90–91	6–8	0.25–2.0	max 0.05
Type 2	90–93	5–7.5	1.5–3.0	max 0.05
Type 3	95–98	1.0–3.0	1.0–2.0	max 0.05

PEWTER SHEET

Pewter sheet is not necessarily produced in standard
thicknesses, as on a commercial basis the
manufacturer rolls to a customer's requirement. As a
guide, a comparison of standard gauges and
equivalent thicknesses is given for sheets in common
use in the pewter workshop.

Gauge numbers and approximate equivalents

Gauge No.	Birmingham		Brown and Sharp	
	mm	in.	mm	in.
10	3.40	0.134	2.59	0.102
12	2.77	0.109	2.05	0.081
14	2.11	0.083	1.63	0.064
16	1.65	0.065	1.29	0.051
18	1.25	0.049	1.03	0.040
20	0.89	0.035	0.81	0.032
22	0.71	0.028	0.64	0.025
24	0.56	0.022	0.51	0.020
26	0.46	0.018	0.40	0.016

Foil is available in two common sizes: 0.125 mm (0.005 in.)
0.175 mm (0.007 in.)

Approximate weight of pewter discs and sheets in common use

Discs Diameter		Birmingham gauge							
		14		16		18		20	
mm	in.	g	oz	g	oz	g	oz	g	oz
50	2	29	1.00	23	0.80	17	0.60	11	0.40
100	4	132	4.67	104	3.67	78	2.75	57	2.00
150	6	284	10.00	220	7.75	167	5.88	119	4.20
200	8	517	18.25	404	14.25	308	10.88	220	7.15
250	10	794	28.00	624	22.00	472	16.67	336	11.88
300	12	1156	40.75	904	31.88	687	24.25	489	17.25

Sheet Gauge Birmingham	Weight Kilos per sq. m	lbs per sq. ft
14	15.1	3 lbs 2 ozs
16	11.8	2 lbs 7 ozs
18	9.0	1 lb 14 ozs
20	6.0	1 lb 4 ozs

MELTING POINTS

Element	Symbol	°C	°F	Specific gravity
Tin	Sn	232	450	7.3
Bismuth	Bi	271	520	9.8
Lead	Pb	327	621	11.36
Zinc	Zn	419	787	7.14
Antimony	Sb	630	1167	6.62
Aluminium	Al	660	1220	2.70
Silver	Ag	960	1761	10.53
Gold	Au	1063	1945	19.36
Copper	Cu	1083	1981	8.94
Nickel	Ni	1455	2651	8.85
Iron	Fe	1535	2795	7.86

POLISHING SPEEDS
Approximate surface speed of polishing mops

Spindle rpm	Feet per minute Diameter of mop – in.			
	4	6	8	10
1450	1520	2300	3050	3800
2000	2095	3150	4200	5250
2800	2930	4400	5850	7350

Spindle rpm	Metres per second Diameter of mop – mm			
	100	150	200	250
1450	7.6	11.4	15.2	19.0
2000	10.5	15.7	20.9	26.2
2800	14.7	22.0	29.3	36.6

Sources of Supply

UNITED KINGDOM SUPPLIERS

Workshop equipment, tools and materials

Buck & Hickman
Bank House
100 Queen Street
Sheffield S1 2DW

Buck & Ryan
101 Tottenham Court Road
London W1P 9DY

Record Ridgway Tools Ltd
Parkway Works
Sheffield S9 3BL

Tunes Engineering Service Ltd
506–11 Ipswich Road
Trading Estate
Slough
Berks SL1 4EX

Jewellers tools and equipment

H. S. Walsh & Sons Ltd
12 Clerkenwell Road
London EC1

Charles Cooper Ltd
Knights House
23/27 Hatton Wall
Hatton Garden
London EC1N 8JJ

Frank Pike
15 Hatton Wall
Hatton Garden
London EC1N 8JE

Hammers, stakes and mallets

William Whitehouse & Co Ltd
Newlyn Road
Cradley Heath
Warley
West Midlands B64 6BN

Thor Hammer Co Ltd
Highlands Road
Shirley
Birmingham B90 4NJ

Lathes and drilling machines

Myford Ltd
Beeston
Nottingham N69 1ER

Warren Machine Tools
Middle Street
Shere
near Guildford
Surrey GU5 9HF

Charles Taylor Ltd
Bartholomew Street
Birmingham B5 5QN

The 600 Group
T. S. Harrison & Sons Ltd
Heckmondwike
Yorks

Gas torches, melting pots and furnaces

William A. Meyer Ltd
Primus – Sievert
PO Box No 562
9/11 Gleneldon Road
Streatham
London SW16 2AU

Camping Gaz (GB) Ltd
126–30 St Leonards Road
Windsor
Berks

Flamefast Ltd
Pendlebury Industrial Estate
Manchester M27 1FJ

The M. H. Berlyn Co. Ltd
Roe Works
Dudley Road
Halesowen
West Midlands B63 3LR

Langs Ltd
Hanworthy Lane Trading Estate
Chertsey
Surrey KT16 9LZ

Microflame (UK) Ltd
Vinces Road
Diss
Norfolk IP22 3HQ

William Allday & Co. Ltd
Alcosa Works
Stourport-on-Severn
Worcs DY13 9AP

Lost wax and rubber mould casting

Leybourn – Needham Ltd
Old Balshaws Yard
12a Market Street
Altrincham
Cheshire

Dryad Crafts
PO Box 38
Northgates
Leicester LE1 9BU

Hoben Davis Ltd
Spencroft Road
Holditch Industrial Estate
Newcastle-Under-Lyme
Staffs ST5 9JE

V. N. Barrett & Co. Ltd
1 Mayo Road
Croydon
Surrey CR0 2QP

Alec Tiranti Ltd
70 High Street
Theale
Berks

Trylon Ltd
Thrift Street
Woolaston
Northants NN9 7QJ

Ambersil Ltd
Whitney Road
Daneshill
Basingstoke
Hants

Hopkins & Williams
PO Box 1
Romford
Essex RM1 1HA

Silicone Products
5 Cranfield Road
Lostock Industrial Estate
Bolton
Lancs

Centrifugal casting

N. Saunders (Metal Products) Ltd
Enessa Works
Edwin Road
Twickenham
Middlesex TW2 6ST

Pewter and solder – commercial quantities

Fry's Metals Ltd
Tandem Works
Christchurch Road
Merton Abbey
London SW29 2PD

George Johnson & Co. (B'ham) Ltd
Highlands Road
Solihull
West Midlands B90 4LP

– small quantities

Pewtersmith
Greenfields
Old Reddings Road
Cheltenham
Glos GL51 6RZ

Polishing equipment and materials

W. Canning Materials Ltd
PO Box 288
Great Hampton Street
Birmingham B18 6AS

Picador Engineering Co. Ltd
1/22 Ashburton Grove
London N7 7AA

Black & Decker
Bath Road
Harmondsworth
Middlesex UB7 0BX

K. R. Whiston Ltd
New Mills
Stockport
Cheshire SK12 4YA

Sand casting

Foseco Foundries International Ltd
258 Long Acre
Nechells
Birmingham B7 5JR

Fordath Ltd
Brandon Way
West Bromwich B70 8JL

Freslent Ltd
Church Bridge Industrial Estate
Oldbury
Warley
West Midlands B69 4LH

Plaster casting

British Gypsum
Cafferate Works
Beacon Hill
Newark
Nottinghamshire NG24 2JQ

ITALY SUPPLIERS

Centrifugal casting

Cabe di a besana & C snc
Via Milano 44/6
1–20090 Cesano Boscone (ML)
Italy

UNITED STATES OF AMERICA SUPPLIERS

1 Pewter ingots
2 Pewter sheet
3 Solder and fluxes
4 Casting plasters
5 Tools, torches, etc
6 Casting machines and associated supplies

Abbey Materials Co.
116 W 29th Street
New York NY10001
1, 2, 3, 4, 5

Allcraft Tool & Supply Co. Inc.
215 Park Avenue
Hicksville NY11801
1, 2, 3, 4, 5

Anchor Tool & Supply Co. Inc.
231 Main Street (RT 24)
Chatham, NJ07828
1, 2, 3, 4, 5

Belmont Smelting & Refining Works Inc.
320 Belmont Avenue
Brooklyn NY11207
1, 3

Paul H. Gesswein Co. Inc.
235 Park Avenue South
New York NY10003
5

National Cast Products Co. Inc.
Machinery & Supply Division
69 Bath Street
Providence
Rhode Island
6

Ney Smelting & Refining Co.
269 Freeman Street
Brooklyn NY11222
1, 3

A. J. Oster Co.
400 Harris Avenue
Providence
Rhode Island 02909
1, 2

Romanoff Rubber Co.
153 W 27th Street
New York NY10001
6

Southwest Inc.
10803 Composite Drive
Dallas
Texas 75220
2, 3, 4, 5

White Metal Rolling & Stamping Corp.
80 Moultrie Street
Brooklyn NY11222
2, 3

Tekast Industries Inc.
PO Box 677
New Rochelle NY10802
6

Golden Metal Industries
50 Taylor Drive
East Providence
Rhode Island 02916
1, 2

T. B. Hagstoz & Son
09 Sansom Street
Philadelphia
Pennsylvania 19106
5

C. R. Hill Company
2734 West 11 Mile Road
Berkeley
Michigan 48072
5

Meriden Rolling Mills
Meriden
Conn.
1, 2

Bibliography

TECHNICAL

Books

ARMYTAGE, Geo. J., *Metalwork for Schools and Colleges*, Oxford University Press, London, 1945

ATKINS, W. A., *Sheet and Plate Metalwork*, Pitman and Sons, London 1947

BOVIN, Murray, *Centrifugal or Lost Wax Jewelry Casting*, Murray Bovin, New York 1972

BRAUN-FELDWEG, Wilhem, *Metal Design and Technique*, B. T. Batsford, London 1975

BRITTAIN, A. and MORTON, P., *Engraving on Precious Metals*, NAG Press, London 1980

CHAPMAN, W. A. J., *Workshop Technology Parts 1, 2 and 3*, Edward Arnold, London 1951

CHARRON, Shirley, *Modern Pewter Design and Techniques*, David & Charles, Newton Abbot, Devon 1973

COKER, Peter, *Etching Techniques*, B. T. Batsford, London 1976

COOLEY, R. H., *Complete Metalworking Manual*, Arco Publishing, New York 1967

EDWARDS, Rod, *The Technique of Jewellery*, B. T. Batsford, London 1977

FRASER, Reekie R., *Draughtsmanship*, Edward Arnold, London 1968

HEDGES, E. S., *Tin and its Alloys*, Edward Arnold, London 1960

ITR Pub. No 566, *Working with Pewter*, International Tin Research Institute, Middlesex

KAUFMAN, Henry, *The American Pewterer, his Techniques and his Products*, Thomas Nelson, Camden NJ 1970

LEYBOURN, Needham G., *Lost Wax Casting*, Model and Allied Publications, Herts 1977

LOYEN, Frances, *Silversmithing*, Thames & Hudson, London 1980

OSBURN, Burl and WILBUR, Gordon, *Pewter: Spun, Wrought & Cast*, International Textbook, Scranton Pa 1928

OSBURN, Burl, and WILBER, Gordon, *Pewter Working*, Dover Publications, New York 1979

REAGAN, James and SMITH, Earl, *Metal Spinning*, Bruce Publishing, New York 1946

ROMANOFF, Philip, *The Complete Handbook of Centrifugal Casting*, Tab Books, Philadelphia 1981

THOMAS, Richmond, *Metalsmithing for the Artist Craftsman*, Chiltern, Philadelphia and New York 1960

UNTRACHT, Oppi, *Metal Techniques for Craftsmen*, Doubleday, New York 1968

VARHUM, William, *Pewter Design and Construction*, Bruse, Milwaukee 1926

WALKER, John, *Modern Metal Working*, Goodhart–Wilcox, Homewood Ill. 1968

Booklets

Equipment for Centrifugal Casting, N. Saunders Ltd, Twickenham, Middlesex

Cold Cure Silicone Rubber Mould Making, Alec Tirranti Ltd, Theale, Berks

Handbook on Lacquering, W. Canning & Co, Birmingham

Handbook on Polishing, W. Canning & Co, Birmingham

Lost Wax Casting, Barretts of Croydon

White Metal Casting, Barretts of Croydon

Research papers

International Tin Research Institute, Greenford, Middlesex:

No. 155 *The Properties of Tin Alloys*

No. 456 *Melting, Casting and Working of Tin Alloys*

No. 464 *Some Factors Affecting the Directional Properties of Rolled Pewter Sheet*

The Worshipful Company of Pewterers, London:

Investigation into the Mechanical Properties of Pewter

Other publications

Many of the suppliers of materials and equipment provide technical literature relative to their products. It will be found that much of this literature contains not only specific information, but also general information of interest to the craftsman.

HISTORICAL

Books

BRETT, Vanessa, *Phaidon Guide to Pewter*, Phaidon Press, Oxford 1981

COTTERELL, Howard H., *Old Pewter: Its Makers and Marks*, B. T. Batsford, London 1929

COTTERELL, Howard H., *National Types of Old Pewter: Revised and Expanded*, The Pyne Press, Princetown 1972

ENGLEFIELD, Elsie, *A Short History of Pewter*, The Priory Press, London 1933

163

HAEDEBE, Hans Ulrich, *Zinn Sammehn*, Emil Volmer Verlag, Munich 1980

HATCHER, J. and BARKER, T. C., *A History of British Pewter*, Longman, London 1974

HOMER, R. F., *Five Centuries of Base Metal Spoons*, Worshipful Company of Pewterers, London 1975

HORNSBY, Peter R. G., *Pewter of the Western World, 1600–1850*, Schiffer Publishing, Pennsylvania 1983

INGLELY-WOOD, L., *Scottish Pewterware and Pewterers*, G. A. Morton, Edinburgh 1907

KEUR, Van Tin, *Uit De Havensteden, Amsterdam, Antwerpen en Rotterdam*, Amsterdam Museum 1979

MASSÉ, H. J. L. J., *Charts on Old Pewter (Revised)*, Ernest Benn, London 1949

MICHAELIO, R. F., *Antique Pewter of the British Isles*, G. Bell, London 1955

MONTGOMERY, Charles F., *A History of American Pewter*, Weathersome Books, New York 1973

OESTRIECH, Helgard, *Edles Zinn*, Emil Volmer Verlag, Wiesbaden 1974

PEAL, Christopher A., *More Pewter Marks and Addenda*, Halesworth Press, Halesworth, Sussex 1976

PEAL, Christopher A., *Let's Collect British Pewter*, Jarrold, Norwich 1977

PEAL, Christopher A., *British Pewter and Britannia Metal*, John Gifford, London 1971

PEAL, Christopher A., 'Roman-British Pewter Plates and Dishes', *Proceedings of the Cambridgeshire Antiquarian Society*, Lx 1967

PEAL, Christopher A., *Pewter of Great Britain*, John Gifford, London 1983

SCOTT, Jack L., *Pewterwares from Sheffield*, Antiquary Press, Baltimore 1980

STARA, *Pewter Marks of the World*, Hamlyn, London 1978

STEMER, Gabriele, *Pewter through 500 Years*, Plenary, Amsterdam 1979

ULLYETT, K., *Pewter Collecting for Amateurs*, Frederick Muller, London 1967

WELCH, Charles, *History of the Worshipful Company of Pewterers Vols I & II*, Blades, East & Blades, London 1902

Papers

'Pewterware of the Worshipful Company of Pewterers', Vols I & II, 1968 and 1979

'British Pewter through the Ages', Reading Museum Exhibition 1969

'Pewterware with Royal Associations', Pewterers' Hall Exhibition 1974

Index

Abrasives *see* Tools
Alloys *see* Pewter
Amalgam—alloy *see* Pewter
Antimony—alloying technique 25
   see also Pewter alloys
Appliqué 62
Association of British Pewter Craftsmen 19

Baluster measure *see* Casting
Bandsaw work 72
Belling out 68
Bench 38
Bewdley pewter 18
Birmingham pewters 19
Bowls 64, 65
Briot—Temperance dish 20
Britannia Metal 18, 23, 27

Casting 90
   Air pressure 128
   Baluster measure 93
   Clothes 90
   Press 105
   Shock 105
   Steam Pressure 117
   Vacuum 117
Caulking 65
Chasing 141
Chemical treatment—colouring 135
Chill blocks 156
Chucks 74, 76
Copper—alloying technique 25

Danforth 22
Danforth and Boardman 23
Decoration—cast 16, 21
Design
   Complex developments 36
   Conical 35
   Cylinder development 35

Drawing circle 32
   Ellipse 32
   Enlargement/reduction 34
   Equipment 32
   Hexagon/octagon 33
   Hollowed articles 36
   Parabola 33
   Pyramid and frustum 35
   Surface development 34, 35
Die stamping *see* Stamping
Dip casting 73
Drill 38
Duncombe 18, 22

Embossing 141, 144, 146
Engraving 145
   Machine engraving 148
Etching
   Acid etching 150
   Photo etching 152
European Pewter Union 19

Felton Frances 23
Files *see* Tools
Fine metal *see* Pewter alloys
Flame sculpture 73
Flame temperatures 48
Flux—zinc chloride 25; grades of 47
Folding bars 57
Formers *see* Tools
Fry's J30 mix 27

Glass bottom base 83
Grinder—bench 38
Guilds 14
   European 19, 21
   Scottish 16

Hammering—booges 15
Hammers *see* Tools

Haseler, J. H. 19
Hinges 63, 64
Hollowing 53
Huguenot craftsmen 16
    Briot 20

Japan Pewterers Association 24

Lacquering 155
Ladle 42, 90
    Whiting coating 92
Lathe 39, 74
    Speeds 94
Ley metal *see* Pewter alloys
Liberty pewter 19
Lubricants 78

Machining 93
Mallets *see* Tools
Matt finish 136
Melting pots 42, 90
Metal moulds 90, 91
    Casting 92
    Cooling 93
Mops 134
Moulding Box 126

Neal, Tom 72
Nuremberg 21

Ordinances 14

Pattern split 122
    Cored 122
Pewter
    Alloys 14, 24, 25, 27, 28, 90
    Design limitations 30
    European 20
    Heat treatment 28
    Ingots 25
    Method of alloying 25, 26, 27
    New techniques of manufacture 17, 18
    Repairs 70
    Repairs antique 71
    Sheet thicknesses 26
    Slabs for sheet manufacture 26
    Superfine Hard Metal 16
    Tonnage 17
Pewterers Company
    Charters 14
    Formation 14
    Number of members 17
Pill boxes 63
Pitchbowl 142
Planishing 55

Plate casting 96
Plating 155
Polishing motor 39
Pressing—forbidden 15; flasks 59

Repoussé 141
Rolling—pewter sheet 25, 26
Rolling edge *see* Spinning

Safety 40, 44, 90, 118, 135
Sandbags *see* Tools
Satin finish 136
Seaming 56
Sheffield 17, 18
Shrinking 68
Snuff boxes 63
Soldering
    Bases 50
    Bench 40
    Body 49
    Feet 49
    Flame temperature 48
    Handle 49
    Side seam 48
    Torches 40, 41, 42
    Turntable 40, 48
Solders 47
Spinning 76
    Bowls and porringers 84
    Chamber candlestick 88
    Coffee pot 86
    Forbidden 15
    High forms 80
    On air 80
    Rolling edge 81
    Sugar bowls 85
    Tankard 82, 83; Georgian style 84
    Teapot 86
Stakes *see* Tools
Stamping—decoration 141, 144, 146
Steam pressure casting 117

Temperance dish 20
Tin mining 13, 25
    Purity 25
    Alloys *see* Pewter alloys
Tools
    Abrasives 45
    Care of 46
    Engraving 146, 147
    Files 44
    Formers 42, 76
    Hammers 45
    Hand 42–6

Hand turning 94
Mallets 46
Raising and forming 42
Repoussé/Chasing 141, 144
Sandbags 42, 43, 143
Saws 43
Snarling iron 143
Snips 43
Spinning 77
Stakes 42
Torches *see* Soldering
Touch marks—Company plates 15
Trifling metal (trifle) *see* Pewter alloys
Tudric pewter 19

Turntable *see* Soldering

Vacuum casting 117
Vice 38

Wax for modelling 101
Whiting *see* Ladles
Wigan 17
Will William 22
Worshipful Company of Pewterers *see* Pewterers Company
Wrigglework 16, 156

Yong Koon 24